SINGING
COWBOY

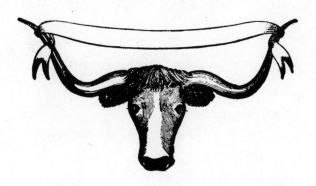

SINGING COWBOY

A BOOK OF WESTERN SONGS

COLLECTED AND EDITED BY

MARGARET LARKIN

OAK PUBLICATIONS   NEW YORK, N.Y.

Guitar Chords Added by: Ethel Raim

Additional Illustrations Selected by: Moses Asch and
                                          Irwin Silber

Published Originally by Alfred Knopf, Inc., 1931

This Edition Published by Special Arrangement With the Author.

This Edition © 1963 by Margaret Larkin

Oak Publications
165 W. 46th Street
New York 36, N. Y.

Library of Congress Card Catalog # 63-23279

LITHO IN U.S.A. 159

At other times, in other places, I have said, ¡*muchas gracias*! to the friends who taught me their songs. I want to add here my thanks to those friends who helped me wrangle the songs into a book; to Witter Bynner, in whose Sante Fe house we laid the first plans; to Carl Sandburg for wise and practical advice as well as for his magical singing; to Robert W. Gordon for his enthusiastic help; to J. Frank Dobie, of the Texas Folklore Society, and to N. Howard Thorpe and Harvey Fergusson, fellow New Mexicans, for suggestions on the glossary; and to Liston M. Oak, who was called upon to criticize and approve every page of this manuscript.

Especially do I thank Helen Black for her skill in the mysterious processes of capturing folk songs for the printed page. Her piano arrangements fit the songs like a saddle fits a bronco.

Miss Black wishes to acknowledge helpful suggestions on the music from John W. Black, her father, Walter S. Charak, of New York, and Francisco Agea, of Mexico City.

Margaret Larkin

CONTENTS

INTRODUCTION

Choosing these songs was not a matter of editorial work; it was a matter of singing. I gathered them with my voice and my guitar, and the basis of choice was that they be worth singing over and over.

There are many cowboy songs besides the ones in this book, and many versions of these. Any listener who can say "That's not the way I heard it" is entitled to his own version, and anyone who says "That reminds me of another song. Did you ever hear this one?" will be carrying on the real business of folk song—the social exchange of music. I hope that some people will have fun with this book, and that others will be so irritated by my personal taste that they will publish their own collections and send me copies.

Although "Singing Cowboy" is not an exhaustive collection, it is a representative one. It contains work songs, love songs, dance tunes, dirges, sentimental ditties, hymns, and narratives of daring deeds. There are some rare songs and many old favorites. Some songs are old and the names of their authors are lost and I have forgotten when I heard them first. Others were written in this decade and fitted to a familiar or a made-up tune.

Cowboy songs are not folk songs in the scholarly sense of the word. Nearly all of them are parodies of old ballads or of popular songs of their day. Some travelled far afield and were shaped by the imaginations of many singers, but most of them became western by a few simple word changes. Older songs were the parent trees, which the western singers budded to new fruits. This sort of borrowing is a usual folk lore process, and if the frontier period had lasted another fifty or hundred years, true folk lore might have emerged. But there was too little time.

The people who made this beginning of folk song were not a homogeneous group. They had no common tradition to draw upon. They had emigrated from every possible condition of life. Young adventurers who hoped for excitement and fortune, men who had failed at more settled occupations, or had been forced out of work by panics and hard times, second generation pioneers who felt that Kentucky, Louisiana, Illinois, and Ohio were getting too crowded, remittance men from England, Irishmen who had fled famine, men who feared the police, peopled the frontier and punched cattle in the early West. Of course they had the common sympathy of occupation, but most young fellows did not stay long at the trade. They acquired cattle of their own, or joined a gold rush, or fought Indians, or with "something tore loose inside" they settled into placid occupation in town. Many died from injuries or exposure, and younger, tougher men took their places at the roundups.

A stable, well-established routine of work is part of the background of folk song. The sea chanteys are based on the work of the sailing vessel; the English ballads are founded on the tasks of an agricultural people. In the early days when its balladry was forming, the cattle country lacked this settled tradition of work. The industry changed radically in each decade. In the 1860's, with unbranded cattle running wild on the Southern ranges, it was feeling for its market. In the 70's it developed the Long Drive to the railroad shipping points as they were pushed through Kansas, and to the good grass lands of Montana and Wyoming. Northern gold rush towns and railroad construction camps made the Long Drive profitable. The United States Government was a large customer, buying beef for the Indians who had been moved from their ancestral hunting grounds to northern reservations to make way for the advancing settlers. These were its great days, when the work of the cattle trade grew specialized and technical, its traditions were formed, and its songs took root. In the 80's cattle ranching became Big Business, administered by Eastern capital and absent owners. The little fellows found themselves losing grass and water. By 1890 the Free Range was going under fence; a cowman had to be able to buy or lease his grazing territory. The Long Drive had almost disappeared with the necessity for it, as the railroads put out spurs to tap the cattle country. This was the end of the isolation that had developed the Westerner as a type, and which, if it had been continued longer, might have nurtured a distinct folk culture.

If cowboy songs may not be classed as folk lore, they nevertheless contain some of its elements. Many of them were group products, and most of them were widely sung, for the cowboy always was an itinerant. They were passed on orally for the most part, and many anonymous personalities added flavor to them. Those that were sung over the widest area are usually the best, but narratives that stayed close at home often contain a vivid bit of history. Although they frequently utter the genteel sentiments of songs of the period from which they derived, they have vigor of their own, and the direct and simple point of view of true folk lore. They deal with the fundamentals, with work, fun, danger, love, money. Sarah D. Lowrie writing in the Philadelphia Ledger, made this astute comment on the tales they tell: "There was one joke— a fall from a bronco; one sorrow—a lonely grave; one temptation— cutting loose in a prairie town; one business—getting the little dogies back and forth to new lands."

English and Scotch ballads, Irish reels, Negro spirituals, German *lieder*, and sentimental songs of the day were the sources of the tunes for cowboy songs. Very few melodies were original; it may be that none of them were. Some were so wrenched out of shape by the demands of their new words as to be nearly unrecognizable, but often the changes were less violent. Most cowboy songs failed to settle down into one generally accepted tune. Even when a ballad became "set" as in the case of "Git Along Little Dogies" so that its main outlines are the same in Montana and Texas versions, it was sung to melodies that were not even distantly related, as well as in greater or less variations of these.

It is curious how indestructible a folk tune may be. For instance, the song "Plantonio" (Page 111) is set to the tune of a 17th century English broadside, "The Waggoner's Boy", which is still sung in Kentucky. The North Carolina mountain folks use it for a song called "Up On Old Smoky". During the Gastonia textile strike in 1929 at the Loray mill, a striker's child, Odel Corley, wrote new words for it, and as "Up In Old Loray", it was sung on the picket lines. Through all these reincarnations, the simple little tune has survived, with only an added trill in the western version. A tune may be like flowing water that carries many kinds of boats at different times.

All lonely people sing, and much of the cowboy's work was done in solitude. Singing relieved the monotony of the night watch, or of the day's ride on the range. Many a puncher who couldn't be got to sing in company if he were roped and hog-tied, sang for his own amusement in the middle of the lone prairie. "I've heared a thousand, but Lord, I kain't sing," says the Old Timer when you ask him for a song. There always were one or two fellows in an outfit who were said to have a voice, and they sang the solo stanzas while the rest of the group joined in Whoopee ti yi yo, or the yell that took the place of a chorus. If there was any accompaniment, it was the guitar, supplemented at dances by a fiddle and an accordion. Fiddling and singing were highly regarded accomplishments, and the cowboy who could do either was in demand at frontier celebrations. While the dancers rested themselves after a furious set, some young buckaroo would sing his favorite "number". Lengthy narrative ballads were most highly esteemed for social purposes, perhaps because they often contained an element of news, and always told a story full of dramatic surprises.

Cowboys disagree as to how much the so-called work songs—like "Git Along Little Dogies", "I Ride an Old Paint", and "The Chisholm Trail"—were actually used in working cattle. Some old timers scorn the notion. They whistled and yelped at their cattle to keep them on the move, or at most employed the eerie, wailing Texas yodel. If they sang, they declare prosaically, it was to keep themselves awake. Others say that they sang to the restless little dogies as they circled the herd at night, and sang and yipped as they drove them forward during the day. The only generalization that one can make is that some cowboys sang to their cattle and others did not. A few songs seem to be designed for the purpose; their rhythms swing to the horse, their stanzas address the cattle directly, their choruses imitate the common cattle calls. But they fall short of being true working songs—they are not geared to the rhythm of the task as a chantey is, or a Negro steel driving song. Perhaps the cowboy's work is not mechanical enough for such intimate connection.

Some writers have thought they detected the rhythms of the horse in the music of cowboy songs. They have even divided them into trotting, walking, and galloping categories. In view of their musical origins, this idea seems to me more romantic than logical. When the pace of the song happens to fit the movements of a horse, it probably is no more than a happy accident.

There is a noticeable absence of the rich man–poor man theme so common to folk song, in the cowboy's balladry. When the songs were forming, there was little distinction between owner and herder. The boss rode with the hands and shared the hardships of the life. Every cow puncher was a prospective cowman; all that was needed to start a herd was a stout rope and a running iron. The range was full of unbranded steers, and while punchers were expected to mark them for the outfit, many owners gave their men permission to brand for themselves over a fixed number. This sort of relationship does not make class-conscious wage workers. The songs record only occasional complaints about the food, and the credit system by which the cowboy drew money in advance against his wages.

"I went to the boss to draw my roll
He had it figured out I was nine dollars in the hole."

Everyone who likes folk songs will like cowboy songs. I have sung them to children, to women's clubs, to audiences of longshoremen and sailors and foreign workers; in lecture halls and drawing rooms and in the theatre; at dude ranches and at real ranches; around campfires; hiking and on horseback. Their free, swinging rhythms never fail to catch the imaginations of the listeners.

And anyone can sing them. It is not necessary to have been born in the West and brought up in the saddle to catch their careless, easy stride. The cowboys themselves have two styles of singing and only two. Either they croon the endless, monotonous stanzas as if they were talking to themselves, or they sing them at a fast trot in tones calculated to reach the other side of a running herd. This has led many people into the mistaken belief that all cowboy songs are sung to one tune.

Singers unfamiliar with them may not know how to render the cowboy yells which occur in some songs. Nonsense words like Coma ti yi youpe are based on cattle calls, and should be half sung and half yelled or talked. The musical notation indicates their approximate tune, and each singer may vary them to suit himself, remembering that they are meant to be full-sized whoops prolonged into singing. In fact, improvisations will always be in order. No two stanzas of any of these songs can be sung exactly with the music as noted for the first stanza. The subtle variations that the words impose upon the tune are what make a simple melody like "Night Herding Song" interesting to sing.

To the cowboy author, the content of the song was more important than the form. If his song came out two lines short at the end he did not trouble to pad it to fit the music. Instead, he repeated as many of the final phrases of the music as were necessary, and considered this a rather elegant finale.

Much of the charm of a cowboy's singing or talking is in his speech inflection, that elusive, native flavor which locality adds to language. There is no way to reproduce it in print; apostrophes and phoneticisms hinder the reader's pleasure and fail to suggest its subtleties. The only exception I have made in ordinary spelling is to write horse as it is invariably pronounced—hoss—to rhyme with boss. It seems particularly unsuitable to pronounce the "r" in this word, although usually the western "r" is not to be overlooked. As in most colloquial American speech, the final letter of "ing" words may be ignored. As for the rest, eastern singers of cowboy songs must be allowed their natural speech, which will not differ from western speech more than the talk of various localities in the west differ from each other.

Cowboys usually enjoy teaching their songs to an unpretentious tenderfoot, but they are likely to criticize Drug Store, Moving Picture and Radio cowboy singers on the ground that they are unable to ride a bucking horse. I have heard some of the best known cowboy singers condemned as follows, "What does he know about cowboy songs? He never was nothing but a honky-tonk singer. He don't know a maverick from a branding iron!"

Although the cow country is not like it was in the old days, and Fords and fences and nearby shipping points have set many a puncher to wrangling dudes, there still are thousands of ranches where cowboys ride herd and sing as the little dogies drift along. For this reason, the old songs survived their period and are apropos even today. The cattle business is founded on an ancient relationship, and the ways of man with his herds and flocks have not changed much since antiquity.

"Abraham emigrated in search of a range,

When water was scarce he wanted a change.
    Isaac owned cattle in charge of Esau,
    And Jacob punched cows for his father-in-law."

The impulse to celebrate his own life in song may not be as urgent as it was, but the cowboy still is adding to his balladry. "Western" poets —Henry Herbert Knibbs, Badger Clark, S. Omar Barker, N. Howard Thorpe, and others—are responsible for many cowboy poems which have been taken over bodily, set to familiar tunes, changed, garbled, localized, and otherwise treated as real folk products. It is astonishing how rapidly they can pass into anonymity. "Little Joe the Wrangler", included in this book, was first published in 1908. Now there are a dozen texts, every cowboy singer knows it, and few remember that it was written by Jack Thorpe. A few other songs now widely sung bear marks of sophisticated composition, but I have not chanced on the names of their authors.

Even less self–conscious and literary are the verses which some cowboy will admit to having made up himself. They may be put to the tune of another cowboy song, to a sentimental air of the 90's, to an outdated jazz hit, or to a melody that is a composite of these. Jack Lambert of Santa Fe, who has punched cattle and wrangled dudes all around the West, gave me such a song, which he had "just thought of" one day when he was riding alone. He sings the stanzas to a Harry Lauder song, and the chorus to that familiar college air, "Didn't He Ramble".

El Vaquero

Oh I once worked in Texas, down on the old H,
In the days when Andy Higgins was our wagon boss,
We rode the grassy prairie and the good old foot hills too
And often did we meet the boys from the Bar C U.

> Oh didn't we ride, we rode,
> We rode the whole day long,
> Singing a cow-boy song,
> Oh didn't we ride, we rode,
> We rode the whole country round.

One day when riding in the rocks, my horse he slipped and fell.
And honest boys, I thought I was bound for the place I will not tell.
They took me to the wagon and stretched a tarp for shade,
For twenty days at Bitter Springs upon my back I laid.

But when my ribs had mended and my head began to clear,
I packed old Buck and saddled Paint, says "Boys, I'm leaving here.
I know not where I'm headed, I'm just going forth,
I may go east, and I may go west, or I may go south or north.

"My trail it may be smooth and straight or it may be full of rocks,
But I think that me and my old Paint horse can stand the hardest knocks.
My path it may be long or short, and it may be wet or dry,"
And I shook my reins and swung my quirt and told them all good-bye.

It is hard to guess how much the interest in singing has declined among the cowboys, since their singing always was incidental to living, and not a matter for special remark. Old books and papers make only casual references to the songs, and people who remember the days of their greatest vigor give varying accounts of them. Cowboys probably sing less nowadays than in the old times—all Americans sing less since modern invention has provided other and more lavish amusements, but I suspect that the decline is less marked among the cowboys than in other groups. Partial isolation helps to keep the songs alive, as well as a conscious feeling that they are valuable as part of the cowboy tradition. They are trotted out along with angora chaps and fancy silk shirts at all Rodeos, Reunions, and Stockmen's Association meetings. The Old Timers collect a bunch of cowboys and soon have them milling to a song, and semi-professional singers twang a guitar and do a nice business on the side in saddles and boots. And sometimes you can surprise a song from a squatting group at a chuck wagon campfire, or from a lone cowboy riding fence. Sit and talk, or better, ride with him, hum an old tune, run through the stanzas, and after a while the most reticent cowboy will begin to criticize your version. If you can once get him to say, "That ain't the way the boys sing it where I come from," you have trapped him into song. I have found that most of the modern cowboys know the old songs, whether or not they will admit to singing, and that they are interested enough to be dogmatic about the local variations.

Besides this casual survival among the cowboys themselves, the songs have a vigorous existence among people who never lived on the range, and are preserved consciously where before they lived of themselves. New Yorkers, Philadelphians, and Bostonians learn them at western dude ranches, where they are as much a part of the background as pack saddles and Indian war-bonnets. Wherever I sing, some guest is sure to lead me to a corner to hum a song learned from a Wyoming dude wrangler. In the West, the boys and girls sing their grandfathers' songs at school picnics and horseback trips. Students in Western colleges wail "The Lone Prairie" along with "Sweet Adeline." People still teach them to one another in the traditional fashion; the singer "learns" you the tune and you "copy off" the words. I always have gathered songs this way, and until I began setting them down for this book, never had written out the songs I knew.

Radio singers and phonograph recordings have popularized cowboy songs, of late years, and have not been without their effect on the folk singers. More than once I have spent a patient hour memorizing a tune, only to have the singer quench my enthusiasm,—"That's the way it goes, and I learnt it off the record." The authority of the record sometimes shakes the folk singers' confidence in their local versions, but revives their interest in the old songs, and their belief in their worth and dignity.

Collection into books is the final and permanent method of preservation. Perhaps the greatest service done the songs in this field is the exhaustive collection which John A. Lomax made many years ago, "Cowboy Songs and Frontier Ballads." It was the first serious effort to preserve them, and still is the classic which all other collectors acknowledge gratefully.

So much sentimental nonsense has been written about the cowboy that one hesitates to set down any estimate of his personality. The cowboys I have known have been gentle, reticent people, not very picturesque, but very charming. Their knowing way with horses,

17

cattle, and dogs, they inherited from several generations of cow persons; one senses a force of tradition behind them. A cowboy on his horse, with his gear fastened to his saddle, is impressively self reliant. He is independent of houses, kitchens, trunks, and tools. Perhaps this distinguishes him from neighboring farmers and townsmen as much as that peculiar quality one always feels in men who spend their lives handling animals.

In the frontier days, when there were Indians to be subdued by bloodshed and fortunes to be made by ruthlessness, cowboys wore two guns and lived by a code of violence. But there was considerable gentility, even on the frontier. Total abstainers were not unknown, though liquor was considered a strong man's relaxation. Murder was condoned only if committed in self defence or to rid the community of a horse thief or a bandit. Cattle rustling, a part of the economy of the industry, was thought of as a misdemeanor, but the horse thief was a serious enemy of society in a country where to be left afoot was to be left for dead. Respect for good women was a cardinal principle of morality, a tradition which still operates with such force that all cowboys apologize at saying damn before a lady. The sterling virtues, so frequently reflected in the songs, might be summarized in an early western epitaph, bestowed upon a fallen hero known as Lonesome Charley. "He never dissipated and always used his own name."

Margaret Larkin

From *Historic Sketches of the Cattle Trade in the West and Southwest,*
by Joseph G. McCoy, the Pioneer Western Cattle Shipper—1874.

"Come along boys, and listen to my tale,
I'll tell you of my troubles on the old Chisholm Trail."

THE CHISHOLM TRAIL
(*First Version*)

The Chisholm Trail, which extended from Texas to the shipping
points of Kansas, was as much a main highway for cattle as the Santa
Fe trail was for commerce. The herds that were driven over it to market
were numbered in thousands. Twenty or thirty cowboys, six or eight
horses to a man, chuck wagons and supplies, made up the trail outfit.
Ten miles a day was good going; the unwieldy caravan made much less
if streams had to be forded. The half wild longhorns were easily stampeded; then the outfit lost a day or two rounding them up or cutting

19

them out of some other herd. A trip up the Chisholm Trail promised danger and excitement and hard work—and pay-off in cash in a wide-open cattle town.

The song of the Chisholm Trail is the cowboy classic; its simple beating tune, its forthright couplets; its "comma-ti-yi-youpy"; its extemporaneous yelps, whoops and yips; its occasional departures from singing into shouting, are as exciting as the clatter of horses' hooves on the hard prairie.

There are hundreds of stanzas and dozens of tune variations according to locality and personal taste. Each outfit added its own doings to the saga; the full version, if one could obtain it, would tell the stories of numberless quarrels, love affairs, night stampedes and hell raisings at the end of the trail.

THE CHISHOLM TRAIL
(*First Version*)

Oh, come along boys, and listen to my tale,
I'll tell you of my troubles on the old Chisholm trail.

 Coma ti ya youpy, youpy ya, youpy ya,
 Coma ti ya youpy, youpy, ya.

I woke up one morning on the old Chisholm trail,
A rope in my hand and a cow by the tail.

Oh, a ten dollar hoss and a forty dollar saddle,
I'm going to punching Texas cattle.

Cloudy in the West and looking like rain,
And my damned old slicker's in the wagon again.

No chaps, no slicker and it's pouring down rain,
And I swear, by God, I'll never night-herd again.

Last night I was on guard and the cattle broke ranks,
I hit my hoss along the shoulders and spurred him in the flanks.

The wind began to blow and the rain began to fall,
And it looked, by God, like we was going to lose 'em all.

I jumped in the saddle and I grabbed a-holt the horn,
I'm the best damned cow puncher ever was born.

I herded and I hollered and I done very well,
Till the boss said, "Boys, just let 'em go to hell."

I'm on my best hoss and I'm going at a run,
I'm the quickest-shooting cowboy that ever drawed a gun.

I went to the boss to draw my roll,
He had it figgered out I was nine dollars in the hole.

I went to the boss to have a little chat,
I slapped him in the face with my big slouch hat.

The boss says to me, "I'll fire you,
Not only you but the whole damned crew."

I'm going to sell my outfit just as quick as I can,
And I won't punch cattle for no damned man.

I'm going to sell my saddle and my bridle right now,
I'll be God damned if I'll punch another cow.

I'm going into town to draw my money,
I'm going into town to see my honey.

With my knees in the saddle and my seat in the sky,
I'm gonna quit punching cows in the sweet bye and bye.

THE CHISHOLM TRAIL
(Second Version)

This version of the old favorite, with its engaging chorus, travelled
a long way before it got to my hands. I learned it from a young Jewish
poet whose name I have forgotten, who had learned it in France from
a Colorado cowboy! The words of the two versions are interchangeable.

THE CHISHOLM TRAIL
(Second Version)

At a good swinging pace, with Bass not too heavy.

Oh, come a-long boys, and lis-ten to my tale, I'll tell you of my

trou-bles on the old Chis-holm trail. Oh tie t'buck t'buck-y,

tie buck - y ru. . . . . tie t'buck t'buck-y ru. . . . .

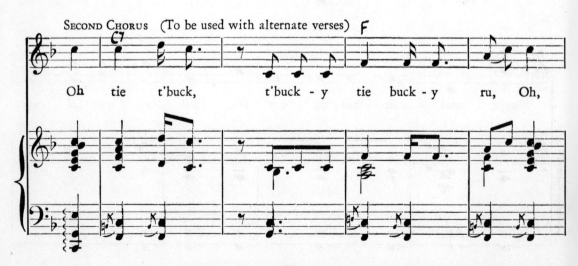

Second Chorus (To be used with alternate verses)

Oh tie t'buck, t'buck - y tie buck - y ru, Oh,

tie   t'buck   t'buck - y   ru.

Oh, come along boys, and listen to my tale,
I'll tell you of my troubles on the old Chisholm trail.

Oh tie t' buck, t'bucky tie bucky ru,
Tie t' buck, t' bucky ru.

I'm up in the morning afore daylight,
Before I sleep the moon shines bright.

Oh, it's bacon and beans most every day,
I'd as soon be eating prairie hay.

Seat in the saddle and hand on the horn,
Best damned cowpuncher ever was born.

Hand on the horn and seat in the saddle,
Best damned cowpuncher ever punched cattle.

I got a gal, prettiest gal you ever saw,
Lives on the bank of the Deep Cedar Draw.

I'll drive them cattle to the top of the hill,
I'll kiss that gal, goddam, I will.

NIGHT HERDING SONG

Range cattle on a strange bed-ground are as nervous as a cat in a new house. They sniff and pace and mill, and any sudden noise—a distant crack of thunder, a coyote wail, a horse shaking his saddle—may set them off in stampede. The cowboys on night herding duty keep up a constant clucking, whistling, crooning and singing to "drown the wild sound" and quiet the cattle, as well as to keep themselves from dozing in the saddle. Any song might be sung for night herding if it has a lonesome sounding tune that can travel as slowly as a walking horse. This song, a weary appeal to the restless little dogies, is a beautiful and touching one.

NIGHT HERDING SONG

Oh say, lit-tle dog-ies, why don't you slow down? You've wan-dered and tramped all ov - er the ground, Oh graze a-long dog-ies, and move kind-a slow, And

don't   be   for - ev - er   on   the   go.   Move   slow,

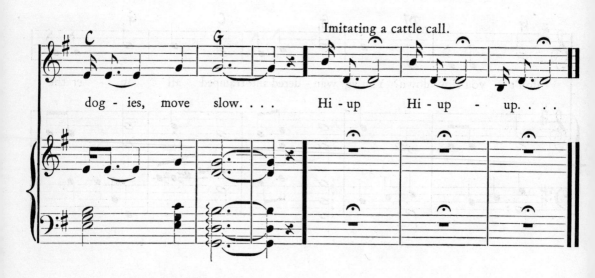

Imitating a cattle call.

dog - ies,   move   slow. . . .   Hi - up   Hi - up - up. . . .

Oh say, little dogies, why don't you slow down?
You've wandered and tramped all over the ground,
Oh graze along dogies, and move kinda slow,
And don't be forever on the go.
Move slow, dogies, move slow!
Hi-up! Hi-up!

I've cross-herded, and trail-herded, and circle-herded, too,
But to keep you together, that's what I can't do.
My horse is leg weary, and I'm awful tired,
But if I let you get away I'm sure to get fired.
Bunch up, little dogies, bunch up!
Hi-up! Hi-up!

Oh say, little dogies, when you going to lay down,
And quit this forever a-sifting around?
My back is weary, my seat is sore,
Oh, lay down, little dogies, like you laid down before.
Lay down, little dogies, lay down!
Hi-up! Hi-up!

Oh, lay still, little dogies, now you have laid down,
Stretch away out on the big, open ground.
Snore loud, little dogies, and drown the wild sound
That will all go away when the day rolls around.
Lay still, little dogies, lay still!
Hi-up! Hi-up!

THE COWBOY'S LAMENT

This version of the more familiar "As I walked out in the streets of Laredo" was given me by a Montana puncher. Some real folk poet must have distilled these rich stanzas from the rather diffuse Laredo incident. I like the deep accents of the tune's last measures, which underscore the tragedy of the tale.

THE COWBOY'S LAMENT

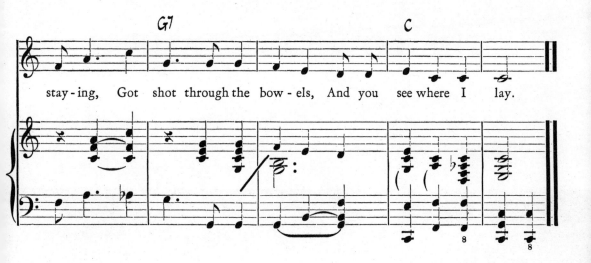

stay - ing, Got shot through the bow - els, And you see where I lay.

My home's in Montana,
I wear a bandana,
My spurs are silver,
My horse is a bay,
I took to card play in
The house I was staying
Got shot through the bowels
And you see where I lay.

Let sixteen gamblers
Lay a hand on my coffin,
Let sixteen cowboys
Come carry me along,
And take me to the graveyard,
And lay the sod o'er me,
I'm just a young cowboy
And I know I done wrong!

Go gather around you
A crowd of young cowboys,
And tell them the story
Of this my sad fate,
Tell one and the other,
Before they go further,
To stop their wild roving
Before it's too late.

It was once in the saddle
That I would go dashing,
'Twas once in the saddle
That I would go gay,
First to the card house
And then to the dram house,
Got shot in the bowels
And you see where I lay.

Then drag your rope slowly
And rattle your spurs lowly,
And give a wild whoop
As you carry me along,
And take me to Boot Hill
And cover me with roses,
I'm just a young cowboy
And I know I done wrong!

From *Historic Sketches of the Cattle Trade in the West and Southwest.*

Swimming the Herd.

I RIDE AN OLD PAINT

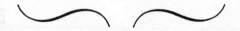

This is a typical riding song—it lopes along gently to the rhythm of the horse. Carl Sandburg, that lusty singer of American folk songs, bestows his highest word of commendation on this song. He calls it a "darb". When he included this version in "The American Songbag", he wrote, "There is rich poetry in the image of the rider so loving a horse he begs when he dies his bones shall be tied to his horse and the two of them sent wandering with their faces turned west".

I RIDE AN OLD PAINT

I ride an old paint, and I

lead an old dam, I'm going to Mon - ta - na for to

throw the hou - li - han, They feed in the cou - lees, and wa - ter in the draw, Their

tails are all mat-ted, And their backs are all raw. Git a - long, you little do-gies, git a -

long there slow, For the fi - ery and the snuf-fy are a - r'ar - ing to go!

I ride an old paint and I lead an old dam,
I'm going to Montana for to throw the houlihan.
They feed in the coulees and water in the draw,
Their tails are all matted and their backs are all raw.

Git along, you little dogies, git along there slow,
For the fiery and the snuffy are a-r'aring to go.

Old Bill Jones had two daughters and a song,
One went to Denver and the other went wrong.
His wife she died in a pool room fight,
But still he sings from morning till night.

Oh when I die take my saddle from the wall,
Put it on my pony, lead him out of his stall,
Tie my bones to his back, turn our faces to the West,
And we'll ride the prairies that we love best.

Ride around the little dogies, ride around 'em slow,
For the fiery and the snuffy are a-r'aring to go.

From *Marvels of the New West*, by William M. Thayer—1887.

Picking up a coin—a cowboy sport.

THE LONE PRAIRIE

It often happens that an earlier song is forgotten, while its parody, a happier combination of music and ideas, lives on in folk lore. Who now remembers to sing "The Ocean Burial, a Favorite and Touching Ballad," which was re-issued in a "new and improved edition", in 1891? Its parody, a very close one, is "Bury Me Not on the Lone Prairie", and every cowboy singer knows it. From a great number of current stanzas, I usually have sung these.

THE LONE PRAIRIE

"Oh, bury me not on the lone prairie,"
These words came low and mournfully,
From the pallid lips of a youth who lay
On his dying bed at the close of day.

He had wailed in pain, till o'er his brow
Death's shadows fast were gathering now,
He thought of his home and his loved ones nigh,
As the cowboys gathered to see him die.

"How oft I remember the well known words
Of the free, wild winds, and the songs of birds,
I think of my home, and the cottage in the bower,
And the friends I loved in my childhood's hour.

"And there is another whose tears will be shed,
For one who lies in a prairie bed,
It pained me then, and it pains me now,
She has curled these locks, she has kissed this brow.

"These locks she has curled, shall the rattlesnake kiss?
This brow she has pressed, shall the cold grave press?
For the sake of the loved ones who will weep over me,
Oh, bury me not on the lone prairie.

"Oh, bury me not on the lone prairie,
Where the wild coyotes will howl over me,
Where the rattlesnakes hiss, and the crow flies free,
Oh, bury me not on the lone prairie!"

From *Historic Sketches of the Cattle Trade of the West and Southwest.*

"Early in the Spring we round up the dogies,
Mark 'em and brand 'em and bob off their tails."

BILLY VENERO

The Cowboy's Reunion at Las Vegas, New Mexico, announces itself as "the saltiest Rodeo on earth, unique and apart from all other cowboy shows, rodeos and exhibitions—the Original and Only Rodeo owned and managed by cowmen and cowboys—real active men of the range."

For nearly twenty years the Reunion has been held annually in Las Vegas. What excitement it brought to our quiet town! The clatter of horses' feet and the whoops of their riders were added to the festive noises of the Fourth of July. Any little girl who had a horse could ride in the Parade. Our gentle Old Bill would snort and r'ar back like a real bronco when the Parade neared Murphy's Corner and the cowboys saluted the judges with pistol shots. The daily programs were doubly thrilling because boys we knew rode their fathers' horses in the races. Year after year we saw the cow hands of nearby ranches compete in the Events.

The western rodeos are a natural outgrowth of round-ups on the open range, when the cowboys of half a dozen ranches competed with each other in throwing the rope and riding the "mean 'uns" of rival outfits. Nowadays the rodeos have moved to town where they take the place of the County Fair or Old Home Week. Although many contestants come from outlying ranches and even from other states, the Las Vegas Reunion has remained local, amateur, and personal. Its audience is composed of fans who follow the fine points of a calf roping contest like baseball crowds follow the World Series.

A rodeo is more than an exhibition; it is a contest of strength and skill. Each Event is run off according to rule. The highly technical feat of bronco busting is governed by twenty-three rules at the Cowboy's Reunion. "Rider will be disqualified for cheating horse in any manner" is typical of the regulations, which besides offering a set of standards for the contestants, aim to give the animal the advantage.

The main features of a rodeo are always racing, bronco riding, steer bulldogging, and roping. Races include quick change relays, chuck wagon relays, and races in which the riders must leap out of bed, pull on boots and chaps, lasso a pony and a pack horse, saddle the one and fasten a tarpaulin on the other, and run the half mile.

Helen Black and I went to the 1930 Cowboy's Reunion looking for cowboy singers. We sat on the contestants' grandstand, between the 'chutes and the race track, and watched bucking hosses, listened to the knowing comments of the hands waiting their turn, laughed when one bronco "a sunfishing son-of-a-gun" whirled like a merry-go-round till his rider jumped for safety and staggered dizzily to his seat.

Reva Cordell, of Bayfield, Colorado, was riding relay races that day. Her slender body poised above a running horse was a pretty sight. Although she looks like the belle of a high-school picnic, she is a trick rider of considerable accomplishment. Riding Roman (standing upright with a foot on each of a pair of galloping horses) standing on her hands in the saddle, crawling under a running horse's neck, are "tricks" she learned to "pass the time" while riding with the cowboys on her father's ranch. While we waited for her race she told us of a sad song that a passing cowboy had sung for her. She had learned the tune and he had written off the words for her, and by the same process she communicated it to us on the contestants' grandstand.

BILLY VENERO

In an A-ri-zo-na town one day, Billy Ve-ne-ro heard them say, That a band of A-pa-che In-dians Were upon the trail of death.

Heard them tell of mur-der done, Three men killed at Roc-ky Run. "They're in dan-ger at the Cow-Ranch," Said Ve-ne-ro un-der breath.

In an Arizona town one day,
Billy Venero heard them say,
That a band of Apache Indians
Were upon the trail of death.
Heard them tell of murder done,
Three men killed at Rocky Run,
"They're in danger at the Cow-Ranch,"
Said Venero under breath.

Cow-Ranch forty miles away,
Was a little spot that lay
In a deep and shady valley
Of the mighty wilderness.
Half a score of homes were there,
And in one a maiden fair,
Held the heart of Billy Venero,
Billy Venero's little Bess.

So no wonder he grew pale,
When he heard the cowboy's tale,
Of the men that he'd seen murdered
The day before at Rocky Run.
"Sure as there's a God above,
I will save the girl I love;
By my love for little Bessie,
I will see that something's done."

Not a moment he delayed
When his brave resolve was made.
"Why man," his comrades told him
When they heard his daring plan,
"You are riding straight to death."
But he answered, "Save your breath.
I may never reach the Cow-Ranch,
But I'll do the best I can."

As he crossed the alkali
All his thoughts flew on ahead
To the little band at Cow Ranch
Thinking not of danger near;
With his quirt's unceasing whirl
And the jingle of his spurs
Little Chapo bore the cowboy
O'er the far away frontier.

Lower and lower sank the sun;
He drew rein at Rocky Run.
'Here those men met death, my Chapo,
And he stroked the glossy mane.
"So shall those we go to warn
Ere the coming of the morn
If we fail—God help my Bessie,"
And he started on again.

Sharp and clear a rifle shot
Woke the echoes of that spot.
"I am wounded," cried Venero
As he swayed from side to side.
"While there's life there's always hope,
Slowly onward I will lope.
If we fail to reach the Cow-Ranch
Bessie Lee shall know I tried."

"I will save her yet," he cried,
"Bessie Lee shall know I tried,"
And for her sake then he halted
In the shadow of a hill.
From his chapareras he took
With weak hands a little book.
Tore a blank leaf from its pages,
Saying "This shall be my will."

From a limb a pen he broke,
And he dipped his pen of oak
In the warm blood that was spurting
From a wound above his heart.
"Rouse," he wrote, "before too late,
Apache warriors lie in wait.
Goodbye, God bless you darling,"
And he felt the cold tears start.

Then he made his message fast,
Love's first message and its last,
To the saddle horn he tied it,
And his lips were white with pain.
"Take this message, if not me,
Straight to little Bessie Lee."
Then he tied himself to the saddle,
And he gave his horse the rein.

Just at dusk a horse of brown
Wet with sweat came panting down
The little lane at Cow-Ranch,
Stopped in front of Bessie's door.
But the cowboy was asleep,
And his slumbers were so deep
Little Bess could never wake him
Though she tried for evermore.

You have heard the story told
By the young and by the old,
Away down yonder at the Cow-Ranch
The night the Apaches came.
Of that sharp and bloody fight
How the chief fell in the fight,
And the panic stricken warriors
When they heard Venero's name.

And the heavens and earth between,
Keep a little flower so green,
That little Bess has planted,
Ere they laid her by his side.

45

ON THE LAKE OF THE PONCHO PLAINS

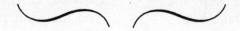

This song is a curiosity. Reva Cordell sent the words with their puzzling references to "swamps of alligators" and the "Cree girl". They stirred dim memories in Helen Black's mind of a song she had heard an uncle sing when she was a child. Her brothers recognized it as "The Lakes of Ponchartrain".

The original hero's adventures took place near New Orleans and the lakes called Ponchartrain, and the heroine was a Creole girl. When the western singers got hold of the song they made suitable changes. The Creole girl became an Indian. Western nomenclature being what it is, "Poncho Plains" (Poncho is a Spanish word for a waterproof cape) did not seem incredible. How the cowboys explained the alligators is a mystery, but cowboys are apt to take their culture for granted, like their God. Other changes in the song include the addition of the first two lines and a general descent from the rather literary language of the original ballad to the vernacular.

ON THE LAKE OF THE PONCHO PLAINS

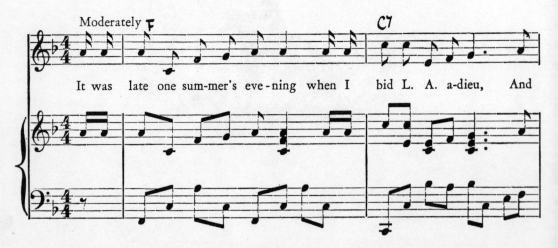

It was late one sum-mer's eve-ning when I bid L. A. a-dieu, And

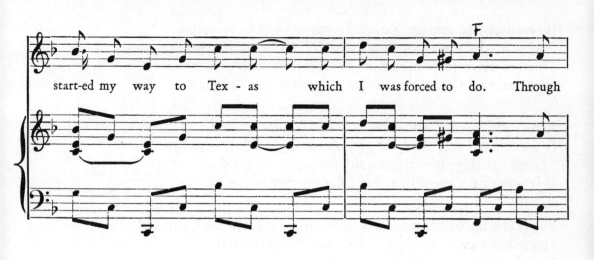

start-ed my way to Tex - as which I was forced to do. Through

swamp of al - li - ga - tors I start-ed my wea - ry way, O - ver

rail - road ties and cross - ings my wea - ry feet did play.

It was late one summer's evening when I bid L. A. adieu,
And started my way to Texas which I was forced to do.
Through swamps of alligators I started my weary way,
Over railroad ties and crossings my weary feet did play.

It was getting late one evening when higher ground I gain,
It was there I met the Cree girl on the Lake of the Poncho Plains.
"Good evening, fair damsel, my money is no good,
If it wasn't for the alligators, I'd sleep out in the woods."

She taken me to her mother's house, they treated me quite well.
Her raven hair in ringlets around her shoulders fell.
I tried to paint her beauty, but I found it was in vain,
Oh, how handsome was that Cree girl on the Lake of the Poncho Plain.

I begged her then to wed me, she said it ne'er could be,
She said she had a lover and he was far at sea.
She said she had a true lover, and true she would remain,
Till he returned to her again in the Lake of the Poncho Plain.

"Adieu to you my pretty miss, I may never see you more,
But I'll always remember the kindness that was shown by your cottage door.'
It's around the flaming circle, a cup to my lips I drain,
Drink success to the beautiful Cree girl on the Lake of Poncho Plain.

From *The New Pictorial Family Magazine, Established for the Diffusion of Useful Knowledge*, Volume IV—1847.

"Shorty grabbed a lariat and roped the Zebra Dun."

ZEBRA DUN

A tenderfoot on a bucking horse is the funniest sight a cowpuncher ever hopes to see. More than one song has been written around this perennial joke. The hero of this incident was luckier than most. My guess is that he was one of those young adventurers who looked like a greenhorn and talked like a dude but who had learned to sit a horse while riding to hounds in the English countryside. The bronco of the song was a dun-colored horse bearing the Z Bar brand. His name was easily corrupted and nowadays the singing cowboys always call him Zebra Dun.

ZEBRA DUN

Moderately fast

We was camped on the plains at the head of the Cim - ar -ron, When a - long come a stran - ger and stopped to ar - gue some. He looked so ver - y fool - ish, we be -

gan to look a-round, We thought he was a green-horn just es-caped from town

We was camped on the plains at the head of the Cimarron,
When along come a stranger and stopped to argue some.
He looked so very foolish, we began to look around,
We thought he was a greenhorn just escaped from town.

He said he'd lost his job upon the Santa Fe,
Was going 'cross the plains to strike the Seven D,
He didn't say how come it, some trouble with the boss,
But asked if he could borrow a fat saddle hoss.

This tickled all the boys to death, they laughed in their sleeves.
"We will lend you a fine hoss, fresh and fat as you please."
Shorty grabbed a lariat and roped the Zebra Dun
And give him to the stranger and waited for the fun.

Old Dunny was an outlaw, had grown so awful wild,
He could paw the moon down, he could jump a mile,
Dunny stood right still as if he didn't know,
Until he was saddled and ready for to go.

When the stranger hit the saddle, Dunny quit the earth,
And travelled right straight up for all that he was worth,
A-pitching and a-squealing and a-having wall-eyed fits,
His hind feet perpendicular, his front feet in the bits.

We could see the tops of the mountains under Dunny every jump,
But the stranger was growed there like the camel's hump.
The stranger sat upon him and curled his black mustache
Like a summer boarder waiting for the hash.

He thumped him in the shoulders and spurred him when he whirled,
And hollered to the punchers, "I'm the wolf of the world."
And when he had dismounted once more upon the ground
We knew he was a thoroughbred and not a gent from town.

The boss who was standing 'round watching at the show,
Walked up to the stranger and said he needn't go,
"If you can use the lasso like you rode old Zebra Dun,
You're the man I'm looking for since the year one."

There's one thing and a sure thing I've learned since I've been born,
Every educated feller ain't a plumb greenhorn.

THE DREARY LIFE

This ironic ditty is a blow at the glamorous West of the tenderfoot's imagination. Indeed, the dreary, dreary life here depicted is truer to the facts than movie fans might think. The cowboy's work was always hard, uncomfortable, and dangerous. But characteristically, he here describes it to an impudent, rollicking melody.

THE DREARY LIFE

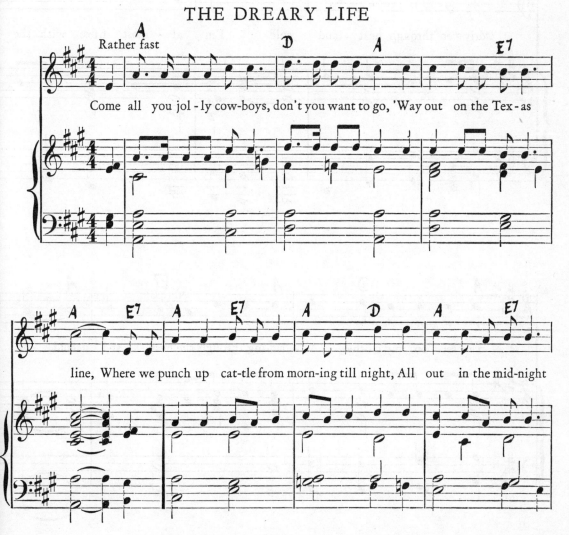

Come all you jol-ly cow-boys, don't you want to go, 'Way out on the Tex-as line, Where we punch up cat-tle from morn-ing till night, All out in the mid-night

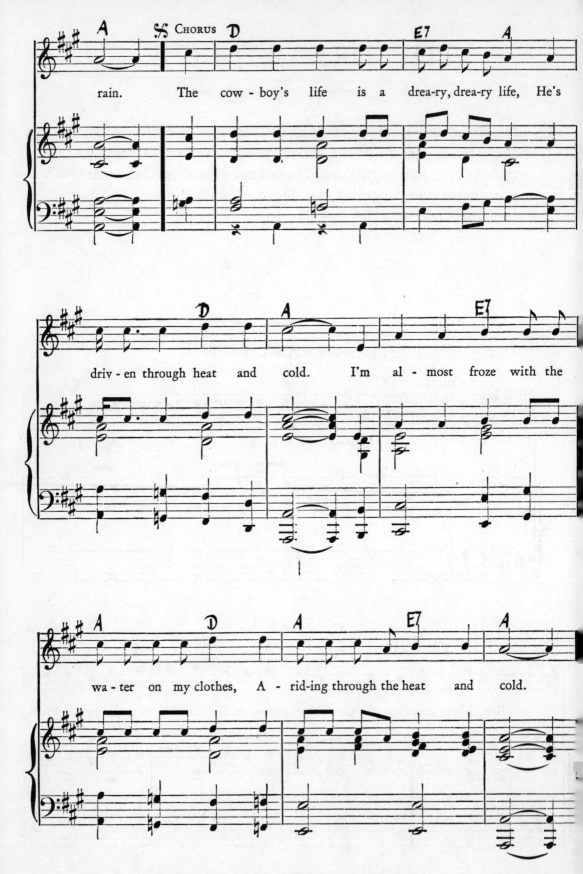

cow-man's ad-vice, And al-ways, al-ways, al-ways, al-ways, al-ways stay at home.

Come all you jolly cowboys, don't you want to go,
'Way out on the Texas line,
Where we punch up cattle from morning till night,
All out in the midnight rain.

   The cowboy's life is a dreary, dreary life,
   He's driven through heat and cold,
   I'm almost froze with the water on my clothes,
   A-riding through the heat and cold.

The wolves and the owls with their terrifying howls
Disturb us in our midnight dream,
When we're laying on our slickers on a cold, rainy night,
'Way over on the Pecos stream.

   The cowboy's life is a dreary, dreary life,
   He's driven through heat and cold,
   I'm almost froze with the water on my clothes,
   A-riding through the heat and cold.

Half past four and we hear the cook roar,
"Wake up boys, it's near the break of day,"
And you've got to rise with those sleepy feeling eyes,
The sweet dreamy night passed away.

   The cowboy's life is a dreary, dreary life,
   He's driven through heat and cold,
   While the rich man's a-dreaming on his velvet couch,
   A-dreaming of his silver and his gold.

Talk about your farms and your city charms,
Talk about your silver and your gold,
Take a cow-man's advice and get a rich and lovely wife,
And always, always, always stay at home.

    That's a cowman's advice, take a cowman's advice,
    And always, always, always, always, always stay at home.

From *Historic Sketches of the Cattle Trade in the West and Southwest.*

"The first time I saw him was early last Fall,
He was swinging the ladies at Tomlinson's ball."

MY LOVE IS A RIDER

This dashing piece of coquetry is said to have been composed by Belle Starr, a notorious woman outlaw of Texas and Indian Territory. She began her spectacular career as a girl spy for Quantrill's rebel band; she married a cattle thief; and finally turned rustler herself, presiding over a band of rascals with the manners of a grand lady and the vocabulary of a frontier hell-cat. Her photographs show her riding a side saddle with a shooting iron on her hip and an ostrich feather in her hat. Although circumstances turned her to a life of violence, she had a taste for the refinements; she had been raised a lady. It would have been just like her to make these revelations from "a young maiden's heart" on one day, and to hold up a poker game and make off with the jack pot the next.

MY LOVE IS A RIDER

My love is a rid - er, wild

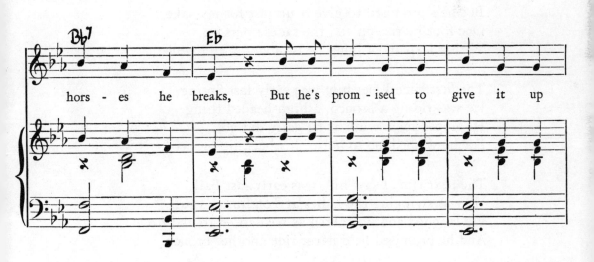

hors - es he breaks, But he's prom - ised to give it up just for my sake, One foot he ties up and the sad - dle puts

on, With a leap and a jump, he is mount-ed and gone.

My love is a rider, wild horses he breaks,
But he's promised to give it up just for my sake.
One foot he ties up and the saddle puts on,
With a leap and a jump he is mounted and gone.

The first time I met him was early last Spring,
He was riding a bronco, a high-headed thing.
He tipped me a wink as he gaily did go,
For he wished me to notice his bucking bronco.

The next time I saw him was early last Fall,
He was swinging the ladies at Tomlinson's ball.
We laughed and we talked as we danced to and fro,
And he promised he'd never ride another bronco.

He made me some presents among them a ring.
The return that I made him was a far better thing.
'Twas a young maiden's heart I would have you all know,
He has won it by riding his bucking bronco.

Now listen young maidens where e'er you reside,
Don't list to the cowboy who swings the rawhide.
He'll court you and pet you and leave you and go
Up the trail in the Spring on his bucking bronco.

From *Historic Sketches of the Cattle Trade in the West and Southwest.*

"Come and git it before I throw it out."

TRAIL TO MEXICO

Ruth Bell of Monterey, California, has gathered up songs in every western state, as she accompanies her husband, a famous trick roper, to summer rodeos. One of those singers who disclaims ability to sing, she hummed tunes for us with sensitive attention to pitch and beat. This is her brilliant version of the Trail to Mexico.

TRAIL TO MEXICO

I made up my mind .... in the ear - ly morn, ... To leave the
home ... where I was born, ... To leave my na - - tive home for a-
while, ... And trav - el west .... for man-y a mile. ......

I made up my mind in the early morn,
To leave the home where I was born,
To leave my native home for a while,
And travel west for many a mile.

'Twas in the year of '83,
That A. J. Stinson he hired me,
He said "Young man, I want you to go,
And follow my herd to Mexico."

'Twas in the springtime of the year,
I volunteered to drive the steers,
I'll tell you boys, 'twas a long hard go,
As the trail rolled on into Mexico.

When I arrived in Mexico,
I wanted my girl, but I could not go,
So I wrote a letter to my dear,
But not a word from her did I hear.

So I returned to my one time home,
Inquired for the girl whom I adore,
She said "Young man, I've wed a richer life,
Therefore young fellow, go and get another wife."

"Oh curse your gold and your silver too,
Oh curse the girl who won't prove true,
I'll go right back to the Rio Grande,
And get me a job with a cowboy band."

"Oh Buddy, oh Buddy, oh please don't go,
Oh please don't go to Mexico,
If you've no girl more true than I,
Oh please don't go where the bullets fly."

"If I've no girl more true than you,
If I've no girl who will prove true,
I'll go right back where the bullets fly,
And follow the cow trail till I die."

From *Historic Sketches of the Cattle Trade in the West and Southwest.*

"Stay at home in Texas
  Where work lasts the year around,

And you'll never get consumption
  From sleeping on the ground."

THE TEXAS COWBOY

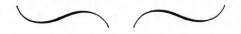

The fierce pride of a Texan in the Lone Star State seems to exceed the local patriotism of other sections of our country. That empire of prairie land retains its peculiar individuality. It breeds men with long, rangy, outdoor bodies, and their own speech, half Yankee nasal, half Southern drawl. The Mexicans along its borders used to have a saying "He's not an American; he's a Texan."

In spite of its jigging tune, this is a homesick song. It should be sung with a faint overlay of sadness as Ruth Bell sang it to me in Santa Fe.

THE TEXAS COWBOY

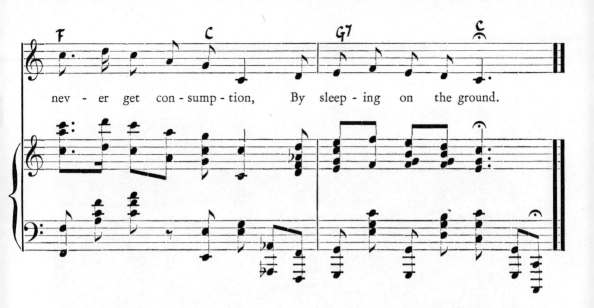

nev - er get con - sump - tion, By sleep - ing on the ground.

Oh, I'm a Texas cowboy,
Far away from home,
If I ever get back to Texas,
I never more will roam.

Montana is too cold for me,
The winters are too long,
Before the roundups do begin,
Your money is all gone.

I've worked down in Nebraska,
Where the grass grows ten feet high,
And the cattle are such rustlers,
They seldom ever die.

I've worked up in the sand hills,
And down upon the Platte,
Where the cowboys are good fellows,
And the cattle always fat.

I've travelled lots of country,
Nebraska's hills of sand,
Down through the Indian Nation
And up the Rio Grande.

But the Bad Lands of Montana
Are the worst I've ever seen,
The cowboys are all tenderfeet,
The dogies are all lean.

Work in Montana
Is six months in the year,
When all your bills are settled,
There's nothing left for beer.

Come all you Texas cowboys,
And warning take from me,
And do not go to Montana
To spend your money free,

But stay at home in Texas
Where work lasts the year around,
And you'll never get consumption,
By sleeping on the ground.

From *Marvels of the New West*, by William M. Thayer, 1887.

Saving a steer bogged down at the water hole.

WINDY BILL

The plot of this story turns on a nicety; no one knows what the outcome would have been if Windy Bill had kept his catch rope free in his hand instead of tying it hard and fast to his saddle horn. Besides the fun of a practical joke on a boastful stranger, the anecdote is valuable as an argument against the Texas practice of tying hard and fast, which many cowpunchers deplore. The song is as full of cowboy technicalities as a *cholla* is of thorns.

WINDY BILL

Wind-y Bill was a Tex-as boy, Said he could rope, you bet,

Said the steer he could-n't tie, He hadn't met up with yet. Us

boys we knew of an old black steer, A sort of an old out-law, That

ran down in the *Mal Pa - ís* at the bot - tom of the draw.

Windy Bill was a Texas boy,
Said he could rope, you bet,
Said the steer he couldn't tie,
He hadn't met up with yet.
Us boys we knew of an old black steer,
A sort of an old outlaw,
That ran down in the *Mal País*
At the bottom of the draw.

This old black steer had stood his ground
With punchers from everywhere,
So we bet old Windy two to one
That he couldn't tie that steer.
Then Bill saddled up his old gray hoss,
His withers and back were raw,
Prepared to tackle this old black steer
That ran down in the draw.

With his grazing bits and his Sam Stack tree,
His chaps and taps to boot,
And his old maguey tied hard and fast,
Bill swore he'd get that brute.
Bill sorta sauntered 'round him first,
The steer began to paw,
Threw his tail up skyward,
And went drifting down the draw.

The old cow hoss flew after him
Like he'd been eating corn,
And Bill, he piled his old maguey
Around old Blackie's horns.

The old-time hoss he set right down,
The cinches broke like straw,
The Sam Stack tree and the old maguey
Went drifting down the draw.

Bill, he lit in a pile of flint,
He got his face some scratched,
He said he always could tie a steer
But this one was his match.
He paid his bets like a gentleman,
Without a bit of jaw,
And said old Blackie was the boss
Of everything down that draw.

There's a moral to my story, boys,
And that you all must see,
Whenever you go to tie a steer,
Don't tie him to your tree;
But take your dally weltas,
That's the California law,
And you'll never see your Sam Stack tree
Go drifting down the draw.

BROWN-EYED LEE

This unhappy narrative is said to be based on an actual lover's quarrel in Bell County, Texas, and to have been composed by the un-lucky suitor himself. It came to me from Robert H. Wruble, who sometimes can be badgered into picking up his guitar, and singing, with head thrown back and eyes squinted shut, from his large collec-tion of American ballads. The song was first noted down for the Texas Folklore Society, by Dr. L. W. Payne, Jr. of the University of Texas.

BROWN-EYED LEE

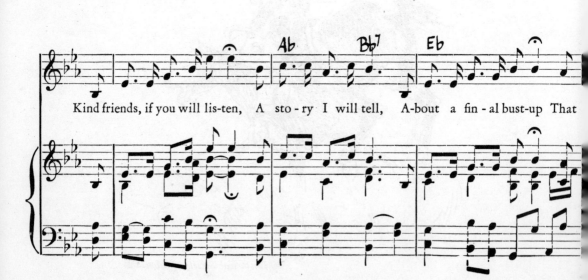

Kind friends, if you will lis-ten, A sto-ry I will tell, A-bout a fin-al bust-up That

Kind friends, if you will listen,
A story I will tell,
About a final bust-up
That happened down in Bell.

I courted a brown-eyed angel
That went by the name of Lee,
And when I popped the question,
She said she'd marry me.

I went out and bought the licence,
March, eighteen ninety nine,
Expecting in a few more days
That darling would be mine.

Her mother grew quite angry,
And said it could not be,
She said she had another man
Picked out for brown-eyed Lee.

She talked to friends and neighbors,
And said that she would fight,
She said she'd get her old six-shooter out,
And put old Red to flight.

But lovers laugh at shooters,
And the old she-devil too,
I said I'd have my darling,
If she didn't prove untrue.

I borrowed Dad's old buggy
And got Jim's forty-one,
And started down to Kerns's
Thinking I would have some fun.

I'm not the one to craw-fish
When I am in a tight,
I said "I'll have my angel
And not be put to flight."

I went on down to Kerns's,
With the devil in my head,
I said "I'll have my darling,
Or leave the old folks dead."

Good fortune fell upon me,
My darling proved untrue,
I give her back her letters,
And bid her a fond adieu.

I pressed her to my aching heart,
And kissed her a last farewell,
And prayed a permanent prayer to God
To send her Ma to hell.

I sold my cows to J. M. G.
My corn to K. M. P.
And cursed the day that I first met
That darling angel Lee.

I sold my horse and saddle
And caught a north bound train,
Leaving that darling girl behind
That I had loved in vain.

When I got up next morning
To see what I could see,
Well every sound that I could hear
Would speak the name of Lee.

I stepped into a billiard hall,
Thinks I, "I'll have a game,"
But every ball that I would knock
Would speak the same dear name.

Although I'm broken hearted,
There's one thing I know well,
That the one that caused this bust-up
Will some day scorch in Hell.

She'll cast her eyes to heaven,
To Jesus on his throne,
And ask for a drop of water
To cool her scorching tongue.

But Jesus will answer her,
"Go to the Old Scratch.
You are the very hypocrite
That busted up this match.

"Depart from me, ye cursed,
You are the Devil's own.
Old Red shall find a resting place
On the right hand of my throne."

And every night I go to bed
I pray a permanent prayer
For the girl I loved so well
With dark brown eyes and hair.

RUSTY JIGGS AND
SANDY SAM

Which makes the better puncher, a big feller or a wiry feller? This question is a hardy perennial on the cattle ranges. The big fellers have pretty much the best of it; they are so nearly in the majority that slighter physiques are usually penalized as "Shorty," or "Slim." Jack Lambert, of Santa Fe, is one of the big fellers. Horses and cattle, dogs, people and automobiles are equally responsive to him.

Jack admitted to whistling and fooling with a guitar but singing ("My goodness gracious!") was outside his line. It took as much gentling as Jack gives a young bronco to ease him into a song.

This ballad, which he learned from Everett Cheetham, the well-known cowboy singer, amused Jack particularly. He liked the fantastic word "cowpography." One of the characteristics of modern cowboy ballads is their use of slang words like "cowpography" and technical phrases like "built him a hole in his old seago" which means to coil a rope ready for throwing.

RUSTY JIGGS AND SANDY SAM

A - way up high in the Sir - ey Peaks, Where mountain pines grow tall,

San-dy Sam and Rus-ty Jiggs Had a round-up camp last fall. They tail.

Away up high in the Sirey Peaks,
Where mountain pines grow tall,
Sandy Sam and Rusty Jiggs
Had a round-up camp last fall.

They had their ponies and their running irons
And maybe a dog or two,
And they 'llowed they'd brand every slick-eared dogie
That came within their view.

Now every old dogie with long flop ears
That didn't hole up by day,
Got his long ears trimmed and his old hide scorched
In the most artistic way.

Says Sandy Sam to Rusty Jiggs
As he threw his seago down,
"I figures I'm tired of cowpography,
And reckons I'll go to town."

So they saddled their ponies and struck a lope,
For it was quite a ride,
But them was the days when an old cowpunch
Could wet his dry inside.

Well, they started in at Kentucky Bar
Up at the head of the row,
And ended up at the Depot House
Just seventy drinks below.

As they was a-coming back to camp,
A-carrying that awful load,
Who should they meet but the Devil himself,
A-walking down the road.

Says the Devil to them, "Now you cowpunching skunks,
You'd better hunt your holes,
For I've come up from the rim-rocks of Hell
To gather in your souls."

"The Devil be damned," says Sandy Sam,
"Though I know that we are tight,
No Devil ever killed an old cowpunch
Without one hell of a fight."

So he built him a hole in his old seago,
And he threw it straight and true,
And he caught the Devil by both horns,
And he had it anchored too.

Now Rusty Jiggs was a reata man
With his gut-line coiled neat,
So he shook it out and he built him a hole,
And he snared that Devil's hind feet.

So they stretched him out and they tailed him down,
And they got their irons red hot,
And they put a swallow fork in each ear,
And they scorched him up a lot.

Then they left him there in the Sirey Peaks,
Necked up to a big black oak,
Left him there in the Sirey Peaks,
Tied knots in his tail for a joke.

Now if you're ever up in the Sirey Peaks,
And you hear one helluva wail,
You'll know that it's the Devil himself,
Crying 'bout the knots in his tail.

WALKING JOHN

Not all of the songs sung by the cowboys are traditional. A number of modern ballads have been taken over bodily and set to a "made up" tune or an old melody. The poems of Henry Herbert Knibbs have been plagiarized and adapted so often that he is entitled to be named the poet laureate of the cowboys. Jack Lambert first sang "Walking John" for me; then I traced it through Everett Cheetham to Arizona where it got its rippling tune, and finally to Mr. Knibbs, who wrote it and who says that it is the biography of a real horse.

Horses are whimsical beasts; they have a sense of humor that other animals seem to lack. Walking John amused himself by bucking off cowboys, while respecting the weaknesses of dudes. I grew up on a horse who held to the opposite point of view. Old Bill was willing, stout, and strong when he respected his rider, but he would take an inexperienced stranger out to the prairie and walk 'round and 'round in ever narrowing circles. Finally he would stop, hang his head, and go to sleep. If his exasperated rider tried to punish him with quirt or spurs, he would pitch gently and amble off to the home corral.

(Words used by arrangement with Houghton Mifflin Company).

WALKING JOHN

Now Walking John was a big rope hoss,
From over Morongo way,
When you laid your twine on a raging steer,
Old John was there to stay.

So long as your rope was stout enough,
And your terrapin shell stayed on,
Dally welta or hard and fast,
'Twas all the same to John.

When a slick-eared calf would curl his tail,
Deciding he could not wait,
Old John forgetting the scenery
Would hit an amazing gait.

He'd bust through them murderous *cholla* spikes,
Without losing an inch of stride,
And maybe you wished you were home in bed,
'Cause partner, he made you ride.

Now John was willing, stout, and strong,
Sure-footed and Spanish broke,
But I'm telling the cockeyed world for once,
He sure did enjoy his joke.

Whenever the morning sun came up
He would bog his head right down
Till your chaps stuck out like angel's wings,
And your hat was a floating crown.

Now that was your breakfast, regular,
And maybe you fell or you stuck,
At throwing a whing-ding, John was there,
A-teaching the world to buck.

But after he'd got it off his chest,
And the earth came back in sight,
He'd steady down like an eight-day clock,
When its innards are oiled and right.

We give him the name of Walking John
Once during the round-up time,
Back in the days when beef was beef,
And John was in his prime.

Now Bob was limping, Frank was sore,
And Tex he could not walk,
When some one says "Call him Walking John,
'Cause he's making so many walk."

But shucks! he was sold to a livery
Which was will ng to take the chance
On John becoming a gentleman
And not scared of them English pants.

Perhaps 'twas the sight of them toy balloons,
That is worn on the tourist's legs,
Kept John a-guessing; from that time on,
He went like he walked on eggs,

As smooth as soap till a tourist guy
Bogged down in a pair of chaps,
The rest of his ignorance plumb disguised
In the rig that he wore, perhaps,

Came floundering up to the livery
And asked for to see the boss,
But the boss he savvied his number right,
And give him a gentle hoss.

Now Walking John had never pitched
For a year come first of June,
But I'm telling the knock-kneed universe,
He sure recollected soon.

For somebody whanged the breakfast gong,
Though we'd all done had our meat,
Old John started to bust in two
With his fiddle between his feet.

That dude spread out like a sailing bat,
Went floating across the sky,
He wasn't dressed for to aviate,
But partner, he sure did fly.

We picked him out of a *cholla* bush,
And part of his clothes stayed on,
We felt of his spokes and wired his folks,
It was all the same to John.

GREAT GRAND-DAD

Jack Lambert contributed this pioneer ballad in which the grand old man of the good old times takes on the heroic proportions suitable to folk ballads.

GREAT GRAND-DAD

Great grand-dad when the land was young, Barred the door with a wa-gon tongue, For the times was rough and the redskins mocked, And he

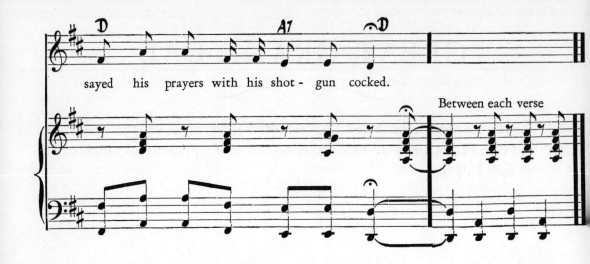

sayed   his   prayers with his shot - gun cocked.

Between each verse

Great grand-dad when the land was young,
Barred the door with a wagon tongue,
For the times was rough and the redskins mocked,
And he sayed his prayers with his shot-gun cocked.

He was a citizen tough and grim,
Danger was duck soup to him,
He ate corn-pone and bacon fat,
Great grandson would starve on that.

Great grand-dad was a busy man,
He cooked his grub in a frying pan,
And he picked his teeth with his hunting knife,
He wore the same suit all his life.

Twenty-one children came to bless
The old man's home in the wilderness,
Doubt this statement if you can,
Great grand-dad was a busy man.

Twenty-one boys and how they grew,
Tall and strong on the bacon, too.
Slept on the floor with the dogs and cats,
And hunted in the woods in their coon skin caps.

Twenty-one boys and not one bad,
They never got fresh with their great grand-dad,
If they had he'd have been right glad,
To tan their hides with a hickory gad.

He raised them rough but he raised them well,
When their feet took hold on the road to Hell,
He straightened them out with an iron ramrod,
And filled them full of the fear of God.

They grew strong in heart and hand,
Firm foundation of our land,
Twenty-one boys and a great grandson,
He has a terrible time with that one.

From *Historic Sketches of the Cattle Trade*
in the West and Southwest.

"Old John started to bust in two
With his fiddle between his feet."

WAY OUT IN IDYHO

When Indian Territory was the West, there was still the Far West. People who had failed to make a fortune at ranching set off to the frontier to make a fortune at mining; the urge to go west was a catching fever. This sassy bit of song is the record of some pioneer farewell. It came to me from Lynn Riggs, the playwright and poet, who was born in Oklahoma, and who has claimed and put to use a rich heritage of folk lore and song. I sang it in his Oklahoma play, "Green Grow the Lilacs".

'WAY OUT IN IDYHO

Re - mem - ber what I promised you, As we set side by side, Beneath that old per - sim - mon tree, I said I'd be your bride.

'Way out in Id - y - ho, We're com-ing to Id - y - ho, With a

four-horse team, We'll soon be seen, 'Way out in Id - y - ho.

Fare - well, it's moth-er and child, I'm off to stay for a - while, So

won't you kiss me be - fore I go, And call me your dar - ling child.

'Way out in Id - y - ho, We're com-ing to Id - y - ho, With a

four - horse team we'll soon be seen, 'Way out in Id - y - ho.

Remember what I promised you,
As we set side by side,
Beneath that old persimmon tree.
I said I'd be your bride.

    'Way out in Idyho,
    We're coming to Idyho,
    With a four-horse team
    We'll soon be seen,
    'Way out in Idyho.

Farewell, it's mother and child,
I'm off to stay for awhile,
So won't you kiss me before I go,
And call me your darling child.

by Frost—1854.

On the Range of the Buffalo.

THE BUFFALO SKINNERS

I heard this ballad first from Carl Sandburg. He dropped his head over his guitar, peered out from behind his drooping wing of hair, and uttered "the range of the buffalo" in deep and sinister tones that conveyed and multiplied the perils of buffalo skinning. It was superb rendition of a remarkable ballad. Sandburg says, "Its words are blunt, direct, odorous, plain and made-to-hand, having the sound to some American ears that the Greek language of Homer had for the Greeks of that time." The song was first made known by John Lomax.

'Twas in the town of Jacks-bo-ro, In the spring of seven-ty-three, A

man by the name of Cre-go came step-ping up to me, Say-ing,

"How do you do, young fel-low, and how would you like to go, And

spend one sum - mer pleas - ant - ly, On the range of the buf - fa - lo?"

'Twas in the town of Jacksboro, in the spring of seventy-three,
A man by the name of Crego came stepping up to me,
Saying, "How do you do, young fellow, and how would you like to go
And spend one summer pleasantly, on the range of the buffalo?"

"It's me being out of employment," this to Crego did I say,
"This going out on the buffalo range depends upon the pay.
But if you will pay good wages and transportation too,
I think, sir, I will go with you to the range of the buffalo."

"Yes, I will pay good wages, give transportation too,
Provided you will go with me and stay the summer through;
But if you should grow homesick, come back to Jacksboro,
I won't pay transportation from the range of the buffalo."

It's now our outfit was complete—seven able-bodied men,
With navy six and needle gun—our troubles did begin;
Our way it was a pleasant one, the route we had to go,
Until we crossed Pease River on the range of the buffalo.

It's now we've crossed Pease River, our troubles have begun.
The first damned tail I went to rip, Christ! how I cut my thumb!
While skinning the damned old stinkers our lives wasn't worth a show,
For the Indians waited to pick us off while skinning the buffalo.

He fed us on such sorry chuck I wished myself 'most dead,
It was old jerked beef, croton coffee, and sour dough for bread.
Pease River's as salty as hell-fire, the water I never could go,
Oh God, I wished I never had come to the range of the buffalo.

The season being near over, old Crego he did say
The crowd had been extravagant, was in debt to him that day,
We coaxed him and we begged him and still it was no go—
We left old Crego's bones to bleach on the range of the buffalo.

Oh, it's now we've crossed Pease River and homeward we are bound,
No more in that hell-fired country will any of us be found,
Go home to our wives and sweethearts, tell others not to go,
For God's forsaken the buffalo range and the damned old buffalo.

DREARY BLACK HILLS

When the Forty-niners set out for the gold fields of California, they pushed their way through half a continent of wilderness and desert. The gold rush to the Black Hills of the Dakotas twenty years later was assisted by iron rails. Indeed, the railroads did all in their power to persuade fortune hunters to ride West and populate the empty plains through which they had built. Hundreds of unlucky immigrants, stranded far from home, echoed the bitter complaints of this song. Cheyenne, the capitol of the Northwest gold fields, saw many a down-and-outer who pined for his humdrum job back in the States and cursed the "railroad speculators" for their share of his misfortunes.

DREARY BLACK HILLS

Kind friends you must lis-ten to my pit-i-ful tale, I'm an ob-ject of pit-y, I'm look-ing quite stale, I gave up my trade sell-ing

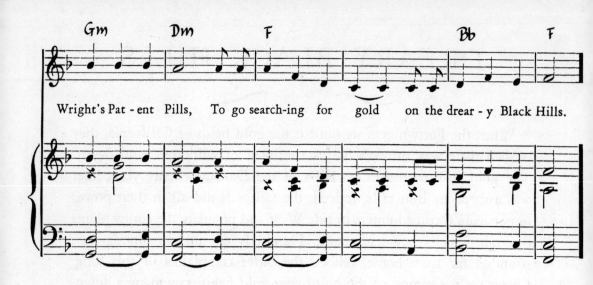

Wright's Pat-ent Pills, To go search-ing for gold on the drear-y Black Hills.

CHORUS

Don't go a-way, stay at home if you can, Stay a-way from that

cit-y they call it Chey-enne, For Wal-i-pe Pete, or Co-

man - che Bill, Will lift off your hair on the drear-y Black Hills.

Kind friends you must listen to my pitiful tale,
I'm an object of pity, I'm looking quite stale,
I gave up my trade selling Wright's Patent Pills,
To go searching for gold on the dreary Black Hills.

Don't go away, stay at home if you can,
Stay away from that city they call it Cheyenne,
For Walipe Pete, or Comanche Bill
Will lift off your hair on the dreary Black Hills.

I got to Cheyenne, no gold could I find,
I thought of the lunch route I'd left far behind,
Through rain, cold, and snow, frozen clean to the gills,
They call me the orphan of the dreary Black Hills.

The round house in Cheyenne is filled every night,
With loafers and bummers of most every plight,
On their backs is no clothes, in their pockets no bills,
Each day they keep starting for the dreary Black Hills.

Kind friends, to conclude, my advice I'll unfold,
Don't go to the Black Hills a-searching for gold,
Railroad speculators their pockets you'll fill
If you go for gold to the dreary Black Hills.

GIT ALONG LITTLE DOGIES
(First Version)

The most dangerous and thrilling cowboy sport is steer bulldogging. The beautiful flight of the pony after the dodging steer; the cowboy's headlong plunge from his saddle to the steer's head; the moment when he dangles under the stubborn neck; the quick, expert twist that throws the animal over; this is bulldogging. It is a sport that the Roman amphitheatres would have applauded—the ancient excitement of direct physical combat between man and beast.

Dee Bibb is the champion bulldogger of the Southwest. At the 1930 Cowboy's Reunion we saw him win the prize money for the fastest time on three steers. "Dee's an all-around hand and he sure can sing fine,' said the other cowboys. So we went to call on him.

Mrs. Bibb sat down at her piano and Mr. Bibb took a "fiddle" out of its case. His great hands that can wrassle a steer or throw a cunning rope dealt gently with the violin. He played old songs and dance tunes with the most surprising embellishments. Though he can't read notes he can fiddle any tune he ever heard, and when he was courting Mrs. Bibb they used to play for all the cowboy dances.

This is his tune for a trail driving song that flourishes in many versions.

GIT ALONG LITTLE DOGIES
(First Version)

rid - ing a - lone, His hat was throwed back and his spurs was a-jing - ling

As he ap-proached me a - sing - ing this song. Whoop-ee ti yi yo yi

CHORUS

yo—— Wy - om - ing will be your new home, Whoop-ee ti yi yo, git a-

long you lit-tle dog-ies For you know Wy-om-ing will be your new home.

As I was awalking one morning for pleasure,
I spied a young cow puncher riding alone,
His hat was thrown back and his spurs was a-jingling,
As he approached me a-singing this song.

    Whoopee ti yi yo yi yo,
    Wyoming will be your new home,
    Whoopee ti yi yo, git along you little dogies,
    For you know Wyoming will be your new home.

Early in the Spring, we round up the dogies,
Mark 'em and brand 'em and bob off their tails,
Round up our ponies, load up the chuck wagon,
And throw the little dogies out on the trail.

    Your mother she was raised way down in Texas,
    Where the jimson-weeds and the cactus grow,
    Now we'll fill you up on prickly pear and *cholla*,
    And throw you on the trail, the trail to Idaho.

It's whooping and yelling and driving the dogies,
Git along, you little dogies, little dogies, git on.
It's whooping and punching and git along you little dogies,
For you know Wyoming will be your new home.

    Whoopee ti yi yo yi yo,
    Wyoming will be your new home,
    Whoopee ti yi yo, git along you little dogies,
    It's your misfortune and none of my own.

GIT ALONG LITTLE DOGIES
(Second Version)

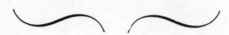

Dee Bibb's "whoopee ti yi yo" calls for a tight rein; its movement is like that of a spirited horse, held back, but straining at the bit. Most old timers sing and yell the song to the following tune, which lunges forward into a good gallop.

The song dates from somewhere in the 1860's—from the days of the Long Trail, when Texas broadhorns were driven to northern markets created by the building of the railroads and the establishment of Indian reservations where "Uncle Sam's Injuns" were fed by the government.

GIT ALONG LITTLE DOGIES (Second Version)

As he ap-proached me a - sing-ing this song. Whoop-ee ti yi yo, git a-

long lit-tle dog-ies, It's your mis-for-tune and none of my own, whoop-ee

ti yi yo, git a-long lit-tle dog-ies. For you know Wyom-ing will be your new home.

As I was a-walking one morning for pleasure,
I met a young cow-puncher a-riding alone.
His hat was throwed back and his spurs was a-jingling,
As he approached me a-singing this song.

Whoopee ti yi yo, git along little dogies,
It's your misfortune and none of my own,
Whoopee ti yi yo, git along little dogies.
For you know Wyoming will be your new home.

Some fellows goes up the trail for pleasure,
But that's where they've got it most awfully wrong,
For you haven't an idea the trouble they give us,
As we go a-driving them dogies along.

Oh, you'll be soup for Uncle Sam's Injuns,
"It's beef, heap beef," I hear them cry.
Git along, git along, you lazy little mavericks,
You're going to be beef steers by and by.

The night's coming on, we'll hold them on the bedground,
These little dogies that roll on so slow.
Round up the herd and cut out the strays,
And roll the little dogies that never rolled before.

From *Historic Sketches of the Cattle Trade in the West and Southwest.*

"Round up the herd and cut out the strays,
    And roll the little dogies that never rolled before."

THE COWBOY'S HEAVEN

The cowboy's parable of the Promised Land is set to a tune that once must have been "My Bonnie Lies Over the Ocean". This is the way it came from Dee Bibb's fiddle.

THE COWBOY'S HEAVEN

In hymn tune style

Last night as I lay on the prai - rie, And looked at the stars in the

sky, ... I won - dered if ev - er a cow - boy . . . . Would

drift to that sweet by and bye. . . . . Roll on,

roll on, Roll on, lit-tle do-gies, roll on, roll on,

Roll on, roll on, Roll on lit-tle do-gies, roll on. . . . .

Last night as I lay on the prairie,
And looked at the stars in the sky,
I wondered if ever a cowboy
Would drift to that sweet by and by.

> Roll on, roll on,
> Roll on, little dogies, roll on, roll on,
> Roll on, roll on,
> Roll on, little dogies, roll on.

They say there will be a great round-up,
And cowboys like dogies will stand,
To be marked by Riders of Judgment,
Who are posted and know every brand.

I know there is many a stray cowboy,
Who'll be lost at that great final sale,
When he might have gone in green pastures,
Had he known of the dim, narrow trail.

For they, like steers that are locoed,
Stampede at the sight of a hand,
Are dragged with a rope to the round-up,
Or get marked with some crooked man's brand.

I'm scared I will be a stray yearling,
A maverick, unbranded on high,
And get cut in the bunch with the rusties
When the Boss of the Riders goes by.

They tell of another Big Owner,
Who's ne'er overstocked, so they say,
But who always makes room for the sinner,
Who drifts from the straight, narrow way.

They say he will never forget you,
That he knows every action and look,
So for safety you'd better get branded,
Get your name in the great Tally Book.

YOUNG COMPANIONS

The wayward boy, who repents on the scaffold and delivers moral platitudes with his expiring breath, is a folk character in all lands. Cowboy balladry is full of horse thieves, murderers, bandits and gamblers who came to this just end. This confession being singularly complete, "Young Companions" is offered as a type. It was first sung to me by Ruth Bell.

YOUNG COMPANIONS

Come all you young com-pan - ions, And lis - ten un - to me, I'll
tell you a sad sto - ry . . . Of some bad com - pa - ny. I was

born in Penn - syl - van - ia   A - mong the beau - ti - ful   hills,   And the

mem - ory   of   my   child - hood   Is   warm with - in   me   still.

Come all you young companions,
And listen unto me,
I'll tell you a sad story
Of some bad company.
I was born in Pennsylvania
Among the beautiful hills,
And the memory of my childhood
Is warm within me still.

I had a kind old mother,
Who oft would plead with me,
And the last word that she gave me,
Was to pray to God in need.
I had two loving sisters,
As fair as fair could be,
And oft beside me kneeling,
They too would plead with me.

I did not like my fireside,
I did not like my home,
I had in view far rambling,
And far away did roam.
I bid adieu to loved ones,
To my home I said farewell,
And I landed in Chicago,
In the very depths of Hell.

It was there I took to drinking,
I sinned both night and day,
But still within my bosom,
A feeble voice would say,
"Oh fare you well my loved one,
May God protect my boy,
May God forever bless him,
Throughout his manhood joy!"

I courted a fair young maiden,
Her name I will not tell,
For I should ever disgrace her,
Since I am doomed to Hell.
It was on one beautiful evening,
The stars were shining bright,
And with a fatal dagger
I bid her spirit flight.

So justice overtook me,
You all can plainly see,
My soul is doomed forever,
Throughout eternity,
It's now I'm on the scaffold,
My moments are not long,
You may forget the singer,
But don't forget the song.

POOR LONESOME COWBOY

This plaintive song is sung in Spanish and in English, and in half a
dozen tunes, all over the West. You can put any amount of self pity into
it; you can embroider upon it so as to express any lack—sweetheart,
horseflesh, another drink, the next meal.

POOR LONESOME COWBOY

1st. & 5th. verses

I'm a poor lone - some cow - boy, I'm a poor lone - some

cow - boy, I'm a poor lone - some cow - boy And a

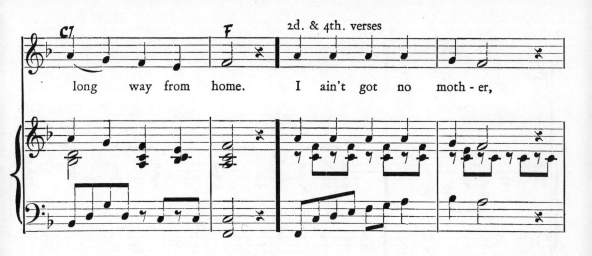

long way from home. I ain't got no moth - er,

I ain't got no moth - er, I ain't got no

moth - er, To buy the clothes I wear.

I'm a poor lonesome cowboy,
I'm a poor lonesome cowboy,
I'm a poor lonesome cowboy,
And a long ways from home.

I ain't got no mother,
I ain't got no mother,
I ain't got no mother,
To buy the clothes I wear.

I ain't got no brother,
I ain't got no brother,
I ain't got no brother,
To ride the steers with me.

And I ain't got no sister,
I ain't got no sister,
I ain't got no sister,
To go and play with me.

I'm a poor lonesome cowboy,
I'm a poor lonesome cowboy,
I'm a poor lonesome cowboy,
And a long day's ride from home.

PLANTONIO

Taos, New Mexico, is a collection of Indian and Mexican towns, where a few Americans live. No railroad comes there; you must drive seventy-five miles along the Rio Grande from Santa Fe, or a hundred miles through the Cimarron pass from Raton, before you come out on its walled-in plain, at the foot of the great Taos Mountain.

Taos was a capitol for the "Mountain Men" when there were still beaver in the streams and traders to buy peltries for fashionable hats. The trappers came back to Taos when the snow began to melt—those lucky ones who had escaped death by starvation, freezing, and Indian arrows. Kit Carson was a "Mountain Man" who set out from Taos every fall with steel traps and returned every spring loaded with rich furs. After the streams had been trapped out and the price of pelts had declined, he became a Scout for the government and put to use the knowledge of Indian fighting that he had gained as a trapper.

In Taos, the grandchildren of the Old Timers ride horseback after school. When they pull up their ponies after a good gallop they sing the old songs. They collect songs from "a boy from Texas" and "a girl from Oklahoma" and any other outlander who has penetrated their ring of mountains. Often they sing songs with local tang and flavor that is missing from more travelled versions.

One of these young custodians of western tradition, Miss Frances Dwire, gave me "Plantonio". This curious name may be the Spanish "Antonio" added to for the sake of alliteration.

PLANTONIO

I'll tell you a sto-ry, There is one I

know, Of a horse I once owned, In New Mex - i - co.

I'll tell you a story,
There is one I know,
Of a horse I once owned
In New Mexico.

Swift as an antelope,
Black as a crow,
Star on his forehead
Was whiter than snow.

His arched neck was hidden
By a long flow of mane,
They called him Plantonio
The Pride of the Plain.

The country was new
And the settlers were scarce,
And the Indians on the warpath
Were savage and fierce.

The captain stepped up,
Said someone must go
For the aid and protection
Of New Mexico.

A dozen young fellows
Straightforward said "Here!"
But the captain saw me,
I was standing quite near.

"You're good for the ride,
You're the lightest one here,
On the back of that mustang
You've nothing to fear."

They all shook my hand
As I nodded my head,
Rode down the dark pathway,
And north turned his head.

The black struck a trot
And he kept it all night,
And just as the east
Was beginning to light

Not a great ways behind
There arose a fierce yell,
And I knew that the redskins
Were hot on my trail.

I jingled the bells
At the end of his rein,
Spoke his name softly
And struck his dark mane.

He answered my call
With a toss of his head.
His dark body lengthened
And faster he sped.

The arrows fell 'round us
Like torrents of rain.
Plantonio, Plantonio,
The Pride of the Plain.

I delivered my message,
And tried to dismount,
But the pain in my foot
Was so sharp I could not.

The arrow you see
Hanging there on the wall,
Had passed through my foot,
Stirrup, saddle and all.

With New Mexico saved
We'd not ridden in vain,
Plantonio, Plantonio,
The Pride of the Plain.

From *Historic Sketches of the Cattle Trade in the West and Southwest*.

"The wind began to blow and the rain began to fall,
And it looked, by God, like we was going to lose 'em all."

UTAH CARROLL

That catastrophe of the range, a stampede, was common enough in the days when cattle were as wild as buffalo and had the run of the unfenced buffalo plains. There are many legends of cowboys who died in turning the running herd. Frances Dwire's version of the death of Utah Carroll is the most complete I have ever heard. The tune given here is from Dee Bibb.

UTAH CARROLL

At a narrative pace

Oh, kind friend you may ask me what makes me sad and still, And

why my brow is dar-kened like clouds up-on a hill, Run

in your po - ny clos - er and I'll tell you the tale, Of

U - tah Carroll my part - ner, and his last ride on the trail.

Oh, kind friend you may ask me what makes me sad and still,
And why my brow is darkened like clouds upon a hill,
Run in your pony closer and I'll tell you the tale,
Of Utah Carroll my partner, and his last ride on the trail.

In a grave without a headstone, without a date or name,
Quietly lies my partner in the land from which I came,
Long, long we rode together, had ridden side by side,
I loved him as a brother, I wept when Utah died.

While rounding up one morning, our work was almost done,
The cattle quickly started on a wild and maddening run,
The boss's little daughter who was riding on that side,
Rushed in to stop the stampede, 'twas there poor Utah died.

Lenore upon her pony tried to turn the cattle right,
Her blanket slipped beneath her, but she caught and held on tight.
But when we saw that blanket each cowboy held his breath,
For should her pony fail her, none could save the girl from death.

When the cattle saw the blanket almost dragging on the ground,
They were maddened in a moment and charged with deafening sound,
The girl soon saw her danger; she turned her pony's face,
And bending in her saddle tried the blanket to replace.

Just then she lost her balance in front of that wild tide.
Carroll's voice controlled the round-up, "Lie still, little girl," he cried.
And then close up beside her came Utah riding fast,
But little did the poor boy know that ride would be his last.

Full often from the saddle had he caught the trailing rope,
To pick her up at full speed was now his only hope.
He swung low from his saddle to take her to his arm,
We thought that he'd succeeded, that the girl was safe from harm.

Such a strain upon his saddle had never been put before,
The cinches gave beneath him and he fell beside Lenore.
When the girl fell from her pony she had dragged the blanket down,
It lay there close beside her where she lay upon the ground.

Utah took it up again and to Lenore he said,
"Lie still," and quickly running waved the red thing o'er his head.
He turned the maddened cattle from Lenore his little friend,
As the mighty herd rushed toward him he turned to meet his end.

And as the herd came on him his weapon quickly drew,
He was bound to die defended as all brave cowboys do.
The weapon flashed like lightning, it sounded loud and clear,
As the cattle rushed and killed him, he dropped the leading steer.

When I broke through that wide circle to where poor Utah lay,
With a thousand wounds and bruises his life blood ebbed away,
I knelt down close beside him and I knew that all was o'er,
As I heard him faintly whisper, "Goodbye, my sweet Lenore."

Next morning at the church yard I heard the preacher say,
"Don't think our kind friend Utah was lost on that great day,
He was a much loved cowboy, and not afraid to die,
And we'll meet him at the round-up on the plains beyond the sky."

LITTLE JOE, THE WRANGLER

The horse wrangler is not often celebrated in cowboy balladry. His position on the range was a humble one; he ranked far above a sheep-herder, but considerably lower than a rider. Nevertheless his duties were arduous. The band of saddle horses in his charge included eight to twelve mounts for each cowboy. Most of these were well trained and reliable, but some were bound to be newly broken broncs, just learning the business. With these beginners, and perhaps a few spoiled horses mixed in the bunch, the *remuda* was likely to be as nervous and hard to hold as the cattle. The cowboys used their horses in strict rotation, and the wrangler was expected to "know them all" and bring them up as needed. In a general emergency he turned out with everybody else in camp, to share the danger of the stampede.

N. Howard (Jack) Thorp, of Socorro, New Mexico, is the author of this celebrated ballad. He wrote it in 1898 "while on trail of O Cattle from Chimney Lake, New Mexico, to Higgins, Texas". It was first put into print in 1908, in "Songs of the Cowboys", a little paper covered book of cowboy songs for which Jack was collector, editor, publisher, and distributor. Cowboys everywhere know and sing it, and it exists now in several versions. This is the original ballad, used with Jack's permission to turn it "wild loose".

(From "Songs of the Cowboys", an enlarged edition, published by Houghton Mifflin Company.)

LITTLE JOE, THE WRANGLER

Lit - tle Joe, the wrang - ler, will nev - er wrang - le more;
His rode up to the herd, On a

days with the *re - mu - da* they are done.
lit - tle old brown pon - y he called Chow;
'Twas a
With his

year a - go last A - pril he joined the out - fit here,
A
bro - gan shoes and ov - er - alls a hard - er - look - ing kid,
You

lit-tle Tex-as stray and all a-lone. 'Twas long late in the even-ing he
nev-er in your life had seen be-fore.

Little Joe, the wrangler, will never wrangle more;
His days with the *remuda* they are done.
'Twas a year ago last April he joined the outfit here,
A little Texas stray and all alone.

'Twas long late in the evening he rode up to the herd
On a little old brown pony he called Chow;
With his brogan shoes and overalls a harder-looking kid,
You never in your life had seen before.

His saddle 'twas a Southern kack built many years ago,
An O.K. spur on one foot idly hung,
While his hot roll in a cotton sack was loosely tied behind,
And a canteen from the saddle horn he'd hung.

He said he had to leave his home, his daddy'd married twice,
And his new ma beat him every day or two;
So he saddled up old Chow one night and lit a shuck this way,
Thought he'd try and paddle now his own canoe.

Said he'd try and do the best he could if we'd only give him work,
Though he didn't know straight up about a cow;
So the boss he cut him out a mount and kinder put him on,
For he sorter liked the little stray somehow.

Taught him how to herd the horses and learn to know them all,
To round 'em up by daylight; if he could
To follow the chuck-wagon and to always hitch the team
And help the *cocinero* rustle wood.

We'd driven to Red River and the weather had been fine;
We were camped down on the south side in a bend,
When a norther commenced blowing and we doubled up our guards,
For it took all hands to hold the cattle then.

Little Joe, the wrangler, was called out with the rest,
And scarcely had the kid got to the herd,
When the cattle they stampeded; like a hailstorm long they flew,
And all of us were riding for the lead.

'Tween the streaks of lightning we could see a horse far out ahead—
'Twas little Joe, the wrangler, in the lead;
He was riding Old Blue Rocket with his slicker 'bove his head,
Trying to check the leaders in their speed.

At last we got them milling and kinder quieted down,
And the extra guard back to the camp did go;
But one of them was missing, and we all knew at a glance
'Twas our little Texas stray—poor Wrangler Joe.

Next morning just at sunup we found where Rocket fell,
Down in a washout twenty feet below;
Beneath his horse, mashed to a pulp, his spurs had rung the knell
For our little Texas stray—poor Wrangler Joe.

FULLER AND WARREN

Cowboys squatting on their heels by the campfire, singing to rest themselves, liked topical songs that connected them with real events. Narratives like this one, telling a true, detailed story about people and places well known to the listeners, were universally popular fifty years ago, and particularly so on the isolated frontier. The report of the fatal interview, the dramatic circumstances of the hero's execution, and the appended moral are characteristic of these old time sensational songs.

FULLER AND WARREN

In-di-a-na state, And a he-ro not man-y can ex-cel. Like

Sam-son he court-ed, made choice of the fair, In-

tend-ing to make her his wife; But she like De-li-lah his

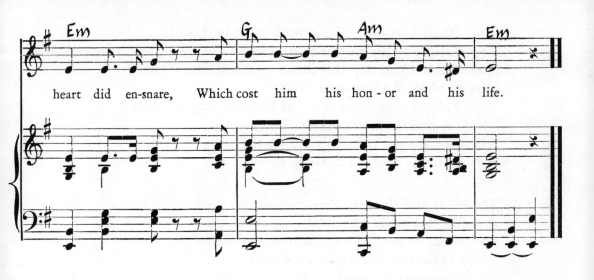

heart did en-snare, Which cost him his hon - or and his life.

Ye sons of Columbia, your attention I crave,
While a sorrowful story I will tell,
Of what happened of late, in the Indiana state,
And a hero not many can excel.
Like Samson he courted, made choice of the fair,
Intending to make her his wife;
But she like Delilah his heart did ensnare,
Which cost him his honor and his life.

He gave her a gold ring in token of his love,
On the face was the image of a dove;
They mutually agreed to get married with speed,
And were promised by the Powers above.
But the light-minded woman she promised to wed
Young Warren who lived in that place.
And that fatal blow caused his overthrow
And made for her shame and disgrace.

When Fuller came to hear he had lost his false dear
Whom he'd vowed by the Powers to wed,
With a heart full of woe to Warren he did go,
And smilingly to him he said,
"Young man, you've done me wrong to gratify your cause
By saying that I left a prudent wife.
So say that you've wronged me, for though I break the laws,
Young Warren, I'll rob you of your life."

Then Warren replied, "Your wish must be denied,
Your darling to my heart she is bound,
And further I may say this is our wedding day,
In spite of all the heroes in town."
Then Fuller in the passion of his love and anger bound,
(Alas! it caused many to cry)
At one fatal shot killed Warren on the spot,
And smilingly said, "I'm ready to die."

The judge and the jury they thought on the case,
A sadder one never was tried,
But Justice demanded both fairness and haste,
And a curse for the false-hearted bride.
For woman can do much to blacken a life
And bring two good friends down to hate.
She'd promised to both that she'd make a good wife,
And now came the terrible fate.

The time it drew nigh when Fuller was to die;
He bid all his audience adieu.
Like an angel he did stand for he was a handsome man,
On his breast he wore a ribbon of blue.
Ten thousand spectators did smite them on the breast,
And the guards had a tear in their eye,
Saying, "Cursed be she who brought this misery,
Would to God it was she who had to die."

The gentle god of Love looked down from above,
The rope flew asunder like the sand.
Two doctors for the pay they murdered him, they say,
And hung him by main strength of hand.
But the corpse it was buried and the doctors lost their prey.
Oh, that woman was bribed, I believe.
Bad women for a certainty are the downfall of men,
As Adam was beguiled by Eve.

From *Historic Sketches of the Cattle Trade in the West and Southwest.*

Chuck Wagon on the Trail.

THE COWBOY

This curious bit of philosophy set to an austere Old English tune was given me by Ruth Bell. The song is often sung to a gayer melody —a corruption of the first four phrases of this one.

THE COWBOY

All day long on the prai-ries I ride, Not e-ven a hound dog to trot by my side, My fire it is kin-dled with chips ga-thered 'round, I boil my own cof-fee with-out be-ing ground, I wash in a pool and I

wipe on a sack, I car-ry my ward-robe all on my back, For
want of an oven I cook in a pot, For want of a bed I sleep on a cot.

All day long on the prairies I ride,
Not even a hound dog to trot by my side,
My fire it is kindled with chips gathered 'round,
I boil my own coffee without being ground,
I wash in a pool and I wipe on a sack,
I carry my wardrobe all on my back,
For want of an oven I cook in a pót,
For want of a bed I sleep on a cot.

My ceiling is the sky, my floor is the grass,
My music the lowing of herds as they pass,
My books are the brooks, my sermons the stones,
My parson's the wolf on his big pile of bones,
My books teach me ever consistence to prize,
My sermons, that small things I should not despise,
My parson remarks from his pulpit of bones,
That Heaven helps them that looks after their own.

Between me and my love lies a gulf very wide,
Some luckier fellow may make her his bride,
My friends gently hint I am coming to grief,
But men must make money and women have beef.
Abraham emigrated in search of a range,
When water was scarce he wanted a change;
Old Isaac owned cattle in charge of Esau,
And Jacob punched cows for his father-in-law.

CALIFORNIA JOE

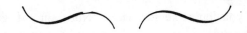

We met Bob Norfleet in the Reunion Headquarters. He had come all the way from Kress, Texas, with two racing horses, and a neighbor boy to ride them. He was not in on the prize money—the high altitude affected his horses' wind—but he was having a fine holiday chinning with other Old Timers.

"I lost my voice forty years ago with the small pox," he said by way of introducing himself to us, "but did you ever hear a song called 'California Joe'?"

The Headquarters was crowded so we adjourned to the sidewalk. We sat down on the running board of an automobile in the main street of Las Vegas and Bob Norfleet began to sing "California Joe". Presently the owner wanted his car so we moved to another running board. The neighbor boy came and said that they must bed the horses. Various cowboys lounged up to listen. "What ye doin', Bob, runnin' a singin' school?" Bob Norfleet sang on, through twenty-three stanzas, until California Joe was safe in the arms of his sweetheart.

The story of California Joe's courtship and marriage was put into verse by Captain Jack Crawford, "The Poet Scout". The hero related it by a campfire at the end of a lucky day in which Captain Jack's scouts had ambushed twenty-three Indians and taken eight scalps.

Captain Jack was a professional Indian fighter, once Chief of Scouts to the U. S. army. All the famous scouts of the time were his friends, Wild Bill Hicock, Jim Bridger, Kit Carson, Buffalo Bill. Nearly half of his verses, which he published in 1891, are memorials to comrades who died violent deaths. In the preface to this poem he records the death of California Joe, who was killed in the same year in which the poem was written, while acting as a guide in the Black Hills. "He was a brave, generous, unselfish man and his only fault was liquor."

Both California Joe and the Poet Scout were well known heroes when Bob Norfleet used to sing this song at dances back in the 1890's. "It was my favorite number," he said. No doubt its popularity was due to its contemporary interest as much as to its spirited narrative.

CALIFORNIA JOE

Well, mates, you don't like sto - ries, Nor am I going to act A

part a - round this camp - fire, That ain't a truth - ful fact. So

fill your pipes and lis - ten, I'll tell you— let me see— I

think it was in fif-ty, From that to six-ty-three.

Well, mates, you don't like stories,
Nor am I going to act
A part around this camp fire,
That ain't a truthful fact.
So fill your pipes and listen,
I'll tell you—let me see—
I think it was in fifty,
From that to sixty-three.

You've all heard tell of Bridger;
I used to run with Jim,
And many a hard day's scouting
I've done along of him;
Well, once near old Fort Reno,
A trapper used to dwell,
We called him old Pap Reynolds,
The scouts all knew him well.

One night in the Spring of fifty
We camped on Powder River,
We killed a calf of buffalo
And cooked a slice of liver.
While eating quite contented,
We heard three shots or four.
Put out our lights and listened,
We heard a dozen more.

We knew that old Pap Reynolds
Had moved his traps up here;
So picking up our rifles
And fixing on our gear
We mounted quick as lightning,
To save was our desire.
Too late, the painted heathen
Had set the house on fire.

We hitched our horses quickly
And waded up the stream,
And there amidst some bushes
I heard a child-like scream,
And there close beside me
A little girl did lie,
I picked her up and whispered,
"I'll save you or I'll die."

Lord, what a ride! Old Bridger
Had covered my retreat;
At times the child would whisper
In a voice so low and sweet,
"Dear Papa, God will take him
To Mama, up above,
There is no one left to love me,
There is no one left to love."

137

The little one was thirteen
And I was twenty-two;
I says, "I'll be your father
And I'll love you just as true."
She nestled to my bosom,
Her hazel eyes so bright
Looked up and made me happy,
Though close pursued that night.

A month had passed and Maggie—
We called her Hazel Eye—
In truth was going to leave us,
Was going to say goodbye.
Her uncle, Mad Jack Reynolds,
Reported long since dead,
Had come to claim our angel,
His brother's child, he said.

What could I say at parting?
Mad Jack was growing old.
I handed him a bank note,
And all I had in gold.
They rode away at sunrise,
I went a mile or two,
And parting says "We'll meet again,
May God watch over you."

By a laughing, dancing brook
A little cabin stood,
Being wearied with a long day's scout
I spied it in the wood.
The pretty valley stretched beyond
The mountains towered above,
And close beside that brookling
I heard the cooing of a dove.

While drinking from my juggery,
And resting in my saddle
I heard a gentle rippling
Like the dipping of a paddle,
And turning to the eddy,
A strange sight met my view,—
A maiden with her rifle,
In a little bark canoe.

She sprang up quick as lightning,
Her rifle to her eye,
I thought for just a moment
My time had come to die.
I offed my hat and told her,
If it was just the same,
To drop her deadly weapon,
For I was not her game.

She dropped her little rifle,
And sprang from the canoe,
She said "I was mistaken,
I taken you for a Sioux.
Your long hair and your buckskin,
Look warrior-like and rough,
My bead was spoiled by sunshine,
Or I'd a-killed you sure enough."

I took her little hand in mine,
She didn't know what I meant,
Although she drew it not away,
But rather seemed content.
One half a glance she gave me,
Her eyes began to fill.
The brook was rippling at our feet,
The dove was cooing still.

It's one more glance she gave me,
And then hung down her head.
"My dear, my bold preserver,
They told me you were dead.
It's been so long, long time, Joe,"
With tear drops in her eye,
I pressed her to my bosom,
My long lost Hazel Eye.

"It's he who claimed me from you
My uncle, brave and true,
Lies sick in yonder cabin,
He oft-times speaks of you.
'If Joe was living, Maggie,'
He said to me last night,
'He'd care for you, dear Maggie,
When God puts out my light.' "

The sun was slowly sinking
In the far-off, glowing West,
We found the old man sleeping,
"Hush, Maggie, let him rest."
Although we talked in whispers,
He opened wide his eyes,
"I had a dream," he murmured,
"I dreamed a dream of lies."

She sprang as quick as lightning
To where the old man lay,
"You had a dream, dear uncle,
Another dream today?"
"Ah yes, I saw an angel
As pure as mountain snow,
And close beside my bedside
Stood California Joe."

"I'm not an angel, uncle,
And that you well do know,
My hands are brown, my arms are, too,
My face is not like snow.
But listen while I tell you,
I have good news to cheer,
Hazel Eye is happy
For Joe is truly here."

It was a few days after,
The old man said to me,
"Dear boy, she is an angel,
As pure as angels be.
For two long months she hunted,
And trapped, and nursed me, too.
God bless you, boy, I believe that
She's happy now with you."

The sun was slowly sinking
When Mag (my wife) and I
Came riding through the valley,
The tear drops in her eye.
"One year ago today, Joe,
I see the mossy grave,
We laid him 'neath the daisies,
My uncle, good and brave."

And, comrades, every spring-time
Is sure to find me there.
A something in that valley
Is always fresh and fair.
Our loves are newly kindled
While sitting by the stream
Where two hearts were united
In love's sweet, happy dream.

139

From *The Poet Scout* by Captain Jack Crawford—1891.

"So fill your pipes and listen."

THE BLACK TAIL RANGE

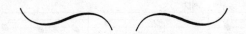

"I'll sing you another song," said Bob Norfleet. "It was back in 1893 that we made up this song in a cow camp in Southern New Mexico. That's where the Black Tail Range is, in the Mogollon Mountains. Every puncher in camp had to make up a verse or else cook. My verse is the second one." He paused, then added reflectively, "I was always falling in love when I was a young feller."

The song pokes a little fun at cow punchers who desert their trade for the uncertain profits of mining.

THE BLACK TAIL RANGE

I am a rov - ing cow - boy Off from the wes - tern plains, My
trade is cinch - ing sad - dles And pull - ing bri - dle reins.
I can throw a las - so With the most grace - ful ease, And

I can rope a bron - co And ride him where I please.

I am a roving cowboy
Off from the western plains,
My trade is cinching saddles
And pulling bridle reins.
I can throw a lasso
With the most graceful ease,
And I can rope a bronco
And ride him where I please.

I started over to the plains
In eighteen-ninety-three,
And the dearest girl in all this world
Fell in love with me.
And if I'd had a little stake,
It's married I thought I'd be,
But the dearest girl in all the world
Went square back on me.

Come all you roving cowboys
You see I'm inclined to roam,
I'm leaving my dear old mother,
Two sisters, and a home,
I'm leaving my dear old mother,
My sweetheart and my home,
To follow the long horned cattle
Until I am too old.

Come all you roving cowboys,
Got mining on the brain,
And when you go prospecting
Cattle on the Black Tail Range,
Then if mining proves unfair
A-hunting you can go,
If you don't kill a mountain sheep,
You'll kill a black-tail doe.

It's when a miner leaves his claim,
He starts out with a whoop,
He doesn't travel very far
Till his toe runs through his boot.
With his pick and shovel on his back
He starts out for his claim,
And with his gun and old case-knife,
He scours the Black Tail Range.

Oh hear that boy a-shouting
Along the Black Tail hill,
"See the mountain sheep I've got,
And the black-tail doe I've killed.'
Down from the rim-rock,
And the game he's left behind
With a mountain sheep's head on his back
And the prospect in his mind.

And when at camp he does arrive,
All from his noble claim,
He'll hear a sample of my mind,
The chief of the Black Tail Range.

WANDERING COWBOY

This tale of a homesick murderer is sung in the Ozark Mountains, as well as further west. It was sent to me by Dr. Vance Randolph, who has collected more than three hundred texts and melodies in the Ozark Mountains, for his anthology "Ozark Mountain Folks", and other books. Dr. Randolph got it from Mrs. Lee Stephens of Jane, Mo., who first heard it about 1899. In Texas, the locale of the murderer's confession is "Slaughter's Ranch."

WANDERING COWBOY

sto - ries and some was sing-ing songs, And some was id- ly smok-ing while the

hours rolled a - long. It's a low and paint-ed cot - tage And far from it I

roam. I'd give my pon - y and sad - dle To be at home sweet home.

We was laying on the prairie at French Ranch one night,
Our heads was on our saddles and our fires was burning bright.
Some was telling stories and some was singing songs,
And some was idly smoking while the hours rolled along.

It's a low and painted cottage
And far from it I roam.
I'd give my pony and saddle
To be at home sweet home.

The boy was young and handsome though his face wore a look of care.
His eyes was the color of heavenly blue and he had light wavy hair.
We asked him why he left his home if it was so dear to him,
He looked at the ground for a moment, his eyes with tears was dim.

Then raising his head, brushed away a tear, and looked the rough crowd o'er,
He says, "Well boys, I'll tell you why I left the Kansas shore.
I fell in love with a neighbor gal, her cheeks was soft and white,
Another feller loved her too, so it ended in a fight.

"But Oh, it makes me shudder for to think of that sad night,
When Tom and me first quarrelled and I struck him with my knife.
In dreams I still can hear Tom's voice when he fell to the ground and said,
'Bob, old boy, you'll be sorry when you see me laying dead'.

"I fell to the ground beside him and tried for to stop the blood
Which was so fastly flowing from his side in a crimson flood.
So now you know the reason why I am compelled to roam,
A murderer of the deepest dye and far away from home."

FAIR LADY OF THE PLAINS

Here is a strange, moaning tune, fit to haunt you at night herding.
Dr. Vance Randolph sent it to me with the comment, "It has been
current near Linn Creek, Missouri, for a great many years; it was
introduced by the Thomas and Waisnor families at least thirty-five
years ago, and was supposedly an old song then."

FAIR LADY OF THE PLAINS

She would drink with me from the cold, bit-ter cup. She loved her red liq-uor which served a man so, She was a fair la-dy, as white as the snow.

There was a fair lady who lived on the plains,
She helped me herd cattle through hard, stormy rains,
She helped me one season through all the round-ups,
She would drink with me from the cold, bitter cup.
She loved her red liquor which served a man so,
She was a fair lady, as white as the snow.

She loved her red liquor which served a man so,
She was a fair lady as white as the snow.
I taught her as a cowboy when the Rangers come 'round,
To use a six-shooter in both of her hands,
To use a six-shooter and never to run,
As long as loads lasted in either gun.

We was going down the canyon in the Spring one year,
To camp there a season with a herd of wild steers,
The Injuns charged on us at the dead hour of the night,
She rose from her slumber the battle to fight.
'Mid lightning and thunder and the downpour of rain
It's in come a bullet and dashed out her brain.

'Mid lightning and thunder and the downpour of rain
It's in come a bullet and dashed out her brain.
I sprung to my saddle with a gun in each hand,
Saying "Come all you cowboys, let's fight for our band."
Saying "Come all you cowboys, let's fight for our life,
These redskins has murdered my darling young wife!"

From *Historic Sketches of the Cattle Trade in the West and Southwest.*

"Git along, you lazy little mavericks,
You'll be beef steers by and by."

TEN THOUSAND CATTLE

I like this fragment of song for its inimitable picture of a reminiscent old bum, leaning on the bar of the "gambling hell" and weeping into his glass over those lost ten thousand. The song was given me by Emile Mardfin, who got it from a Colorado friend.

151

TEN THOUSAND CATTLE

Ten thou - sand cat - tle, gone a - stray, Left my range, and tra-velled a - way, And the sons - of - guns, I'm here to say, Have left me dead broke, dead broke, to-day. In gam-bling hells de-

lay - ing,   Ten   thou-sand cat - tle   stray - ing,   stray-ing.

Ten thousand cattle, gone astray,
Left my range, and travelled away,
And the sons-of-guns, I'm here to say,
Have left me dead broke, dead broke, today.

In gambling hells delaying,
Ten thousand cattle straying.

And my gal, has gone away,
Left my shack and travelled away,
With a son-of-a-gun from Ioway,
And left me a lone man, a lone man today.

In gambling hells delaying,
Ten thousand cattle straying, straying.

Historical Society of Montana

JESSE JAMES

If America ever had a Robin Hood, it was the bandit and train robber, Jesse James, whose life and death are celebrated in this ballad. Jesse's exploits were famous in the West. His insolent robberies caught the imaginations of men used to the petty tricks of the cattle rustler. Like all thieves of folklore, he was kind to the poor. Old Timers who drank with him at some "Last Chance Saloon" will tell you that he always helped a fellow who was down on his luck.

On the fatal Saturday night, Jesse, who was living in St. Joseph under the name of Howard, was standing on a chair hanging a picture for his wife, when Robert Ford shot and killed him through an uncurtained window. The deed was considered the more infamous because Ford had been a member of Jesse's gang and admittedly killed him for the reward.

JESSE JAMES

Jes-se James was a lad who killed man-y a man. He

robbed the Glen-dale train. He stole from the rich and he
gave to the poor, He'd a hand and a heart and a brain.
Jes-se had a wife to mourn for his life, Three

chil-dren, they were brave, But that dir-ty lit-tle cow-ard that

shot Mis-ter How-ard, Has laid Jes-se James in his grave.

Jesse James was a lad who killed many a man.
He robbed the Glendale train.
He stole from the rich and he gave to the poor,
He'd a hand and a heart and a brain.

Jesse had a wife to mourn for his life,
Three children, they were brave,
But that dirty little coward that shot Mister Howard,
Has laid Jesse James in his grave.

It was Robert Ford, that dirty little coward,
I wonder how he does feel,
For he ate of Jesse's bread and he slept in Jesse's bed,
Then he laid Jesse James in his grave.

Jesse was a man, a friend to the poor.
He'd never see a man suffer pain,
And with his brother Frank he robbed the Chicago bank,
And stopped the Glendale train.

It was on a Wednesday night, the moon was shining bright,
He stopped the Glendale train,
And the people all did say for many miles away,
It was robbed by Frank and Jesse James.

It was on a Saturday night, Jesse was at home,
Talking to his family brave,
Robert Ford came along like a thief in the night,
And laid Jesse James in his grave.

The people held their breath when they heard of Jesse's death,
And wondered how he ever came to die,
It was one of the gang called little Robert Ford,
That shot Jesse James on the sly.

Jesse went to his rest with his hand on his breast,
The devil will be upon his knee,
He was born one day in the county of Shea
And he came of a solitary race.

This song was made by Billy Gashade,
As soon as the news did arrive,
He said there was no man with the law in his hand
Could take Jesse James when alive.

Jesse had a wife to mourn for his life,
Three children, they were brave,
But that dirty little coward that shot Mister Howard,
Has laid Jesse James in his grave.

From *Historic Sketches of the Cattle Trade in the West and Southwest.*

"He always drank good whiskey wherever he might be."

SAM BASS

Like Jesse James, Sam Bass was a bank and train robber, who was betrayed by a member of his own gang. His career was brief. In less than a year after his boldest crime—the holdup of a Union Pacific train—he had spent his share of the loot, $20,000, had gone back to raiding and robbing, had skirmished with the Texas Rangers, and was dead. His end was brought about by Jim Murphy, one of his gang who had been captured in a fight with the Rangers. The song says that Jim consented to give information to the authorities in exchange for his freedom because he owed Sam money, but this is not on the official record. In any case, he kept his bargain, and when Sam, with Barnes and Jackson, rode in to rob the bank at Round Rock, the Rangers were on hand. One of them rushed out of a barber shop with lather on his face and killed Barnes and mortally wounded Sam, who died the next day, July 21, 1878.

This one-sided gun battle was typical of the Texas Rangers, who often were outnumbered three to one, or fifty to one in their battles with outlaws and Indians. It is reminiscent of that tall Texas tale of the lone Ranger who was sent to quell a riot, and who, when chided for not bringing reinforcements, replied, "Hell, there ain't but one riot, is they?"

SAM BASS

Sam Bass was born in In-di-an-a, it was his na-tive home, And at the age of sev-en-teen young Sam be-gan to roam. He

first came out to Tex-as a cow-boy for to be,

kind-er-heart-ed fel-low you sel-dom ev-er see.

Sam Bass was born in Indiana, it was his native home,
And at the age of seventeen young Sam began to roam.
He first came out to Texas a cowboy for to be,
A kinder-hearted fellow you seldom ever see.

Sam used to deal in race stock, he owned the Denton mare,
He matched her in scrub races and took her to the Fair.
He fairly coined the money and spent it frank and free.
He always drank good whiskey wherever he might be.

Sam left where he was working one pretty morning in May,
A-heading for the Black Hills with his cattle and his pay.
Sold out in Custer City and then got on a spree,
A harder set of cowboys you seldom ever see.

A-riding back to Texas they robbed the U. P. train,
For safety split in couples and started out again.
Joe Collins and his partner were overtaken soon,
With all their hard-earned money they had to meet their doom.

Sam made it back to Texas all right side up with care,
Rode into the town of Denton with all his friends to share.
Sam's life was short in Texas; three robberies did he do,
The passenger and Express cars and U. S. Mail Car too.

Now Sam he had four partners, all daring, bold, and bad,
There was Richardson and Jackson, Joe Collins and Old Dad.
Four more bold and daring cowboys the Rangers never knew;
They whipped the Texas Rangers and dodged the boys in blue.

Sam had another companion called Arkansas for short,
But Thomas Floyd, the Ranger, cut his career quite short.
Oh, Tom is a big six-footer and think's he's mighty fly,
But I can tell you his racket,—he's a deadbeat on the sly.

Jim Murphy was arrested and then let out on bail,
He jumped the train for Terrell after breaking Tyler jail.
Old Major Jones stood in with Jim and it was all a stall,
A put-up job to catch poor Sam, before the coming Fall.

Sam met his fate at Round Rock, July the twenty-first.
They pierced poor Sam with rifle balls and emptied out his purse.
Poor Sam he is a dead cowboy and six feet under clay,
And Jackson's in the mesquite trying to get away.

Jim had borrowed Sam's good gold and didn't want to pay,
His only idea it was to give brave Sam away.
He sold out Sam and Barnes and left their friends to mourn,
Oh, what a scorching Jim will get when Gabriel blows his horn.

Perhaps he's got to heaven, there's none of us can say,
But if I'm right in my surmise he's gone the other way.

I'M BOUND TO FOLLOW THE LONG HORN COW

Carl Sandburg gave me this ballad, from the manuscripts of Franz Rickaby. It is kin to *The Roving Cowboy* and *The Black Tail Range*, and the *Lone Star Trail*, having a little blood and bones from each of these songs. The line, "If I had a little stake, it's married we should be" is the best loved line in cowboy balladry—it occurs in a dozen songs at least.

I'M BOUND TO FOLLOW THE LONG HORN COW

boss - es they all like me, boys, and say I'm hard to beat, I
al - ways give the brave stand - off— they say I've got the cheek.

I'm bound to follow the long horn cow until I get too old,
Although I work for wages, boys, and get my pay in gold.
My bosses they all like me, boys, and say I'm hard to beat,
I always give the brave stand-off—they say I've got the cheek.

To admire those pretty little girls, I'd like to take me from apart,
I'd work and strive to support her, boys, and love with all my heart.
And if I had a little stake it's married we should be,
For the prettiest little girl that ever I saw she fell in love with me.

She said it 'ud almost break her heart if I should go away,
But I must leave in another week, my boss said so today.
She must cheer up her courage, boys, and choose her another one.
I'm bound to follow the long horn cow until my race is run.

Adieu, kind friends, a blessing now, you see I'm bound to roam,
I'm bound to leave my kind old mother, my sweetheart and my home,
And when I get on my shipping point I'll often shed a tear
For the runaway thoughts of the darling little girl that cares the most for me.

JIM THE ROPER

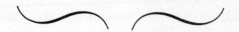

This requiem, celebrating some long forgotten puncher, was recalled for me by E. B. Reddick, who grew up in Indian Territory, and now lives in Taos, New Mexico.

JIM THE ROPER

They dug him a grave at the set of the sun,

His ri-ding was o-ver, his ro-ping was done.

They dug him a grave at the set of the sun,
His riding was over, his roping was done.

Brown-featured and bonnie and strong were those brave
Rough cowboys who gathered around Jim's lone grave.

In silence, grim silence they covered him o'er,
To ride the wild bronco and rope cattle no more.

They turned toward their cabins deserted and grim,
Close by the green grave where they buried poor Jim.

They turned toward their cabins, deserted and lorn,
Since Jim the brave rider and roper was gone.

No sound save the Yellowstone dashing a-foam,
Is heard midst the ruins, once Jim's happy home.

And so went the story and so it still goes,
That Jim's ghost is seen where the Yellowstone flows.

HOME ON THE RANGE

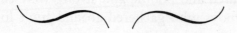

This song is best sung on a rainy afternoon when the taxi-cabs are raising their five o'clock din in Fifth Avenue and the heavy smoky sky predicts that the drizzle will last all night. Under these conditions, singer and audience will cast a homesick, sentimental thought to the bright West. Even if they were born to city pavements, the song is sure to stir them with pleasant nostalgia for freer air and a wider view.

HOME ON THE RANGE

Oh, give me a home where the buffalo roam,
Where the deer and the antelope play,
Where seldom is heard a discouraging word,
And the skies are not cloudy all day.

Home, home on the range,
Where the deer and the antelope play,
Where seldom is heard a discouraging word,
And the skies are not cloudy all day.

The red man was pressed from this part of the West,
It's likely he'll never return,
To the banks of Red River, where seldom if ever
His flickering camp fires burn.

Oh, I love these wild flowers in this dear land of ours,
The eagle I love to hear scream,
I love the red rocks and the antelope flocks,
That graze on the mountain tops green.

Then give me a land where the bright diamond sand
Flows leisurely down the stream,
Where the graceful white swan goes gliding along
Like a maid in a heavenly dream.

GOODBYE, OLD PAINT

This rousing song, squeaked on the fiddle, thumped on the guitar, and roared by the dancers, was often a finale—a "Home Sweet Home" for *bailes* and *juntas* frequented by cowboys. The tradition was that as long as a single dancer could remember or improvise another stanza, the dance would go on. The number of stanzas in existence is countless; these are the indispensable ones. This tune is a New Mexico variant of the one more commonly heard.

GOODBYE, OLD PAINT

Goodbye, old Paint, I'm a-leaving Cheyenne,
Goodbye, old Paint, I'm a-leaving Cheyenne.

I'm a-leaving Cheyenne, I'm off for Montan',
Goodbye, old Paint, I'm a-leaving Cheyenne.

Old Paint's a good pony, he paces when he can,
Goodbye, old Paint, I'm a-leaving Cheyenne.

Go hitch up your hosses and give them some hay,
And seat yourself by me so long as you stay.

My hosses ain't hungry, they won't eat your hay,
My wagon is loaded and rolling away.

My foot's in the stirrup, my bridle's in my hand,
Good morning, young lady, my hosses won't stand.

Goodbye, old Paint, I'm a-leaving Cheyenne,
Goodbye, old Paint, I'm a-leaving Cheyenne.

GLOSSARY

BOOT HILL. The graveyard of a frontier town held the bones of many a young fellow who had passed in his checks at violent work or at violent play and had been buried as he died, with his boots on. The phrase, "to die with your boots on" has a jocose ring, a tinge of bravado that is lacking in the similar saying, "to die in harness." So the term Boot Hill is not a lugubrious one; it suggests a brave, if reckless end, for young hell-raisers who rode into town for a big time and combined too much liquor with their Colt forty-fives.

BRONCO BUSTING. The breaking of young horses to the tasks of a cattle ranch may be done either by the regular cow hands or by a bronc rider, bronc peeler, bronco twister or bronco buster, specially hired for the work.

There is more to bronco busting than the spectacular riding seen at rodeos. First, the horse must learn never to run against the rope, so that he will become a dependable part of that working unit, the mounted roper. A rope attached to the snubbing-post teaches him this lesson. After he has run its length and has tumbled head over heels and choked himself, he understands that the rope is an unbreakable thing, fit to be respected by the stoutest-hearted bronco. So well does he learn submission that ever afterwards he can be restrained by a lariat held withers-high. He may dodge the lasso, but it never will occur to him to slip under or jump over the rope corral. Any bit of rope or leather hanging from his head reminds him of that unconquered snubbing-post: throw his reins down and he will stand "ground tied" all day.

In successive lessons he is shown the hackamore (a bitless rope bridle) and learns to wear it, is shown the saddle and feels its crushing weight and the merciless grip of its cinches.

At last comes the day when the buster mounts him ready to ride it out; he can match every leap, bite, fall, and roll of the wild young pony with a trick of his own. Horses for ordinary use are considered busted after they have been ridden three or four times and the rider can stay on with comparative safety.

On the ranch each rider uses his own methods, but rodeo contests enforce definite rules for bronco busting. A top rider in a rodeo does not "show daylight" nor "pull leather". Fanning with his hat and scratching with his spurs are points of merit that are not necessarily a part of real bronco busting.

When a horse is ruined in the breaking so that he is completely unmanageable, he is called a spoiled horse. An outlaw is a spoiled horse who has killed a rider, or a horse that has joined the wild bunch. The bucking broncos of the rodeos are spoiled horses.

CAVVYARD. *See* Remuda.

CHAPS—CHAPEROS—CHAPARERAS—CHAPARÉJOS. The Mexicans invented the cowboy's long leather leggings, which he wears over his pants to protect him from brush and thorns, from the horns of cattle, from burns by the fast-running rope, and from severe hurt when he is thrown from his horse. They are put on like armor and put off again when work is over, for they are uncomfortable for walking and sitting, and only useful when the cowboy is astride.

Ordinary working chaps are made of heavy calfskin, or goatskin with the hair left on.

When the cowboy is on dress parade, at rodeos, local dances, and other Western functions, he likes to wear his fancy chaps—leather studded with "spots," or angora, dyed a dazzling orange or purple. These are not seen on the range, where he usually works in a pair of dirty pants, unless he actually needs the protection of leather.

CHOLLA. A particularly vicious variety of cactus. The word is Spanish, and is pronounced chóy-a.

CHUCK WAGON—CHOW WAGON—GRUB WAGON. The chuck wagon is the travelling commissary of an outfit riding away from the home ranch for rounding up, branding, or other business. It looks like the old prairie schooner and may be drawn by horses or mules. The presiding cook, often called by the Spanish word, *cocinero,* may be an old-timer, or a puncher whose injuries have retired him from the saddle, or a Negro, a Mex, or a Chinee. His duties include driving the wagon over unbroken prairies, through canyons, and across rivers; rustling wood in treeless country; providing ambulance for an injured rider; and turning out bacon and beans, sourdough biscuits and flapjacks, canned tomatoes and spuds in all weathers. He usually maintains the legendary ill temper of cooks, his only friendly word being "Come and git it before I throw it out."

CINCH. *See* Terrapin Shell.

COCINERO. *See* Chuck Wagon.

COULEE—DRAW. A coulee is a natural depression in the rolling prairie, where water stands during the spring freshets, and grass grows lush through the summer. It is less marked than an arroyo or a gully, which is gashed out by swift water, and in which no grass grows.

A draw is deeper than a coulee; it is almost a ravine. Water runs or stands in it at some times of the year, but it is not a continuous watercourse.

CUTTING. When a cowboy wants a steer for some purpose, he separates him from the bunch by nosing his pony in behind him, first on one side, then on the other, until he edges him out of the herd. A good cutting hoss understands this work perfectly. He quickly sees which animal is wanted and follows with a slow, sidling walk, while in the herd. Once outside, the steer is likely to try to dodge back again; the cutting pony is alert for this peculiarity of steers and pivots on his hind feet—"swap ends"—and turns him back where he is wanted. Horses seem to enjoy this work; they take delight in nipping at the steer as if they recognized the age-old superiority of the herder's horse to the herd.

To be cut in the bunch with the rusties is to be herded with the poorest steers, the culls, the wild ones, the lean ones.

DALLY WELTA—HARD AND FAST. The Dally Welta roper keeps his rope free in his hand until he has caught his animal, then quickly "takes his wraps" around the saddle horn. The words are properly *Dar la vuelta,* from the Spanish, meaning "to give a turn". The most frequent corruption is Dally Welta; others are Dally Wertha, Dolly Wirta, or simply Dally.

The Hard and Fast man, who uses a shorter rope, ties it fast to the saddle horn, claiming that this method saves time, especially if the object is to throw and tie the animal.

DOGIE. The Western definition is "A calf whose mammy has gone off and left it and whose daddy has took up with another cow". It may mean a yearling that has not wintered well, or may refer to any young animal. The cowboys often use the word as an affectionate diminutive—all the herd may be addressed as little dogies much as one calls a favorite dog a pup. The origin of this word is mysterious. Jack Thorpe says, "A dogie, naturally having been short on milk, is pot or dough-bellied. Dogies were formerly called dough-bellied or doughies."

In pronouncing, give the vowel the long O sound; you will be known for a tenderfoot if you call it "doggies".

FIDDLE. A slang word for the horse's head.

A top rider "fights his head" to keep a bronc from putting "his fiddle between his feet", for in this position only the cleverest buster can keep his seat. A novice will fly over the saddle horn.

FIERY AND SNUFFY. I always have supposed that these adjectives referred to the fiery and snuffy hosses, who had been dragged out of the rope corral, cinched into their forty-pound saddles, and were r'aring to be mounted and off after the herd.

GRAZING BIT. An easy curb bit or snaffle, less severe than the savage ring or spade bit.

GUT LINE. *See* Lasso.

HICKORY GAD—IRON RAMROD. Great Grand-dad drew a fine distinguishing line between his punitive instruments. When mere sassiness was involved, he cut the traditional hickory switch, but for offenses that endangered their salvation he inflicted a formidable punishment on his doughty sons. One can believe that they did not often risk a beating with the iron rod that rammed home the powder and shot in the old muzzle-loader.

HOULIHAN. The act of leaping forward to the horns of a steer in bulldogging so as to knock him down is called the houlihan. In rodeos "willful houlihaning" disqualifies the bulldogger, although if he throws the houlihan by accident, he may let the animal up and wrassle him down again in the approved fashion.

KACK. N. Howard Thorpe, who has "put in twenty five years as horse wrangler, cow hand, range boss, trail boss, and manager of different outfits", and is an authority on "Westernisms", is the author of this explanation. "Regarding the word Kack, 'tis an Indian word for canoe. When they first saw a Texas saddle with the horn and cantle sticking up, it reminded them of the high stern and bow of a canoe. I believe the word properly was spelled 'kiack', and any old kind of a Texas saddle used to be called a kack."

LASSO—LARIAT—REATA—MAGUEY—TWINE—SEAGO—GUT LINE—ROPE. All these terms indicate the cowboy's one indispensable tool—his rope. This is usually about thirty feet long and has a reinforced eye at one end through which it turns for a noose. The cowboy carries it coiled at the left of his saddle horn, tied by a strap that is fastened to the saddle for the purpose. He uses it

not only for roping cattle, but for a thousand other errands as well. If wood is needed at the ranch house, he ties his rope to a dry log and "snakes" it behind him. If he wants to make a temporary corral for his "string", the rope serves as walls. It is his constant plaything. Whenever he lacks for amusement, he practices spinning the rope in one of the intricate patterns which the cowboys invented to "keep their hand in".

Ropes are usually made of hemp, but in the old days they were made of buffalo hide, platted rawhide, horsehair, twisted grass, and the Mexican maguey or century plant.

Reata and Maguey are taken directly from the Spanish; Lasso is derived from *el lazo,* seago from *la soga,* and lariat from *la reata.*

Most cowboys say rope when they mean rope, the other terms being considered fancy or slang words, or indicating special uses.

LATIGO. *See* Terrapin Shell.

"LIT A SHUCK THIS WAY". This curious expression puzzled me and I asked Jack Thorpe, the author of the ballad in which it occurs, to explain its meaning. His definition shows it to be one of those curious, roundabout, linguistic twists of which the cowboys are so fond. He says: "The expression originated before the cowpunchers used papers to make their smokes with, and built them out of corn husks or shucks. If you were riding along, had made a cigarette, had placed it in your mouth, you would naturally have your horse headed in the direction you intended going, and would light the shuck—thence, lit a shuck this way."

LOCOED. The loco weed takes its name from the Spanish word meaning mad. When horses or cattle eat its flowers, they go insane—"plumb loco". Their aberrations take several forms. Some are easily frightened and "stampede at the sight of a hand". Some run themselves to death. Some lose all sense of relations in space, and, mistaking an arroyo for a rivulet, fall and break their necks.

When I was a child, our family saga of mountain adventures included the story of a great white pack-horse, whose madness was not discovered until the party was forty miles from town and beyond all possibility of replacing him. On a steep trail that sidled around the shoulder of a mountain so precariously that man and beast could scarcely pass, he suddenly r'ared up on his hind legs in order to get up a six-inch ledge and fell backwards. The pack came off, and skillets and Dutch oven, bedding, tools, and canned goods rolled down the mountain. After two hours of retrieving and repacking the camping-gear, the harassed creature went another hundred yards, and did it again!

Most ranchers shoot locoed horses as soon as they discover their condition, for there is no cure. Cattle seem to eat the weed less frequently.

MAGUEY. *See* Lasso.

MAL PAÍS. These are Spanish words meaning bad country, and the term is applied specifically in the Southwest to the purple lava mesas, which wear out the feet of men and horses.

MAVERICK. A maverick is an unbranded steer, although the term may be applied to any unbranded, and therefore ownerless, animal. Besides this technical meaning the word is used colloquially to indicate an unfortunate person; tramps, wanderers, and ne'er-do-wells are spoken of as mavericks. Or it may be used as an epithet for either beast or man. "You lazy little mavericks!" "You bandy-legged, wall-eyed, lonesome-looking maverick, you!"

There are a dozen stories as to the origin of this word. All Old

Timers agree, however, that Samuel A. Maverick, of San Antonio, Texas, was responsible for its birth. For one or another reason Maverick did not brand his calves, and when neighbors found his young cattle on the range, they would say: "That's a Maverick," and let the calf go, or perhaps, if not quite so honest, would brand it for themselves. The best authenticated story that I have run across recounts how Maverick took over four hundred head in 1845 in payment of a debt and, having little interest in the cattle, left them in charge of a Negro herder. His herder took no interest either and neglected the branding, with the result that when Maverick came to sell his herd eleven years later, it still numbered four hundred head. The increase had drifted away, unbranded. This story was related by a friend of Maverick, in contradiction to those tales that he collected his herd by putting his brand on all the unmarked cattle that came his way.

MILLING. The technique for stopping stampeding cattle is to ride at an angle against the front of the herd in an attempt to turn the leaders back on their own tracks. Once the leading cattle are headed off, the herd starts to run in a circle. Pressed closer and closer upon itself by the cowboys, the herd draws into a close, irregular mass—the mill. Once they get to milling, the cattle slow down and walk until they tire themselves out and are ready to lie down.

OUTLAW. *See* Bronco Busting.

PAINT. A Paint hoss, otherwise called a Pinto, is splashed with more than one color, with black and white, or brown and white. Cowboys entertain a superstition that Paints have less stamina than hosses of a solid color; they prefer a buckskin, a bay, a blue, a roan, a dun, a sorrel. Perhaps this idea grew out of the Indian custom of breeding horses for the splashed hide, and the fact that Indian ponies usually were of inferior stock. This preference of the Indians may be noted still in their modern paintings; the horses they draw are Paints oftener than not. Because of their spectacular appearance, the trick riders of the rodeos like to use nicely marked Pintos.

PITCHED. *See* Whing Ding.

REMUDA—CAVVYARD—CAVVY. The horses that are in use at the ranch or on the trail are kept in a bunch called variously the remuda, from the Spanish, or cavvyard, cavvy, etc., a corruption of the Spanish *caballada,* meaning the horse herd. The former term is used in the Southwest and the latter in the Northwest, although they are interchanged frequently.

At the ranch the horse wrangler rounds up the horses every day or two, to keep them from straying too far, keeping up only such animals as are needed. On the trail the bunch is in charge of a day and a night wrangler, who drive it or graze it, and bring it up whenever the cowboys need a change of mounts. The size of the remuda varies according to the work in hand, but usually will include six to ten horses for each man. Each cowboy uses his "string" in strict rotation, reserving his best mounts for night herding and for cutting. On the Long Drive, horses that showed a particular aptitude for swimming were kept for use at the critical times of getting the herd to take the water when rivers were to be crossed. Besides his more dependable horses, the cowboy's "string" includes two or three freshly broken broncos, who get their training as they work.

ROPE HOSS. A good rope hoss is as valuable to the cowboy as a good cutting hoss; frequently they are the same animal.

When he wants to rope a steer, the cowboy rides after him at top speed, twirling the noose above his head, and guiding the pony by a light touch of the rein or the pressure of his knee. As he makes the cast, he leaps from the saddle, leaving the rope tied in half hitches to the horn. His unfastened reins drop to the ground, and the pony stops dead still, while the cowboy goes down the rope, hand over hand, to tie the animal. As he works to throw the steer or flank the calf, the canny horse helps by keeping the rope taut, but a good roping horse never drags an animal. If the steer is big and active, the horse braces against the rope so hard that he seems to squat on his hind feet—"that wise old hoss, he set right down." In this position he may slowly pivot so as to face the steer and keep the rope from tangling. Roping contests at the rodeos afford beautiful exhibitions of clever roping horses; indeed, the performance of the horse is as important as his own skill to the cowboy who hopes to win the money.

RUNNING IRON. In the earliest days of the cattle business, brands were run with a heated rod of iron, which the cowboy used like a red-hot pencil. Branding by this method was as crude as it was simple, and such brands were easily altered by the cattle-thief who was clever at changing a V to a diamond and a U to an O. Large owners began to have the pattern of their brands made into iron, so that they could be stamped on the hide in one operation. Stamp irons, being less easily altered, were made compulsory by law in many Western states.

RUSTIES. *See* Cutting.

RUSTLER. A man may rustle up some wood, and cattle may rustle for their grass, but when man rustles cattle, a crime is committed.

Cattle Rustlers were not always criminals; they became so by act of law, much as liquor-sellers became bootleggers. After the Civil War the ranges were overrun with unbranded cattle, ownerless because their owners had been called away to war and had neglected the branding. It was legitimate for any man to brand for himself as well as for his owner, or for gratuities paid by the local Stock Associations. This system founded fortunes for penniless men, but it could last only as long as the supply of unbranded cattle. When the West began to settle up, the big owners combined against it. What had been individual enterprise became a crime, and, as always when economic needs conflict with the folk ways, the new order of things met with resistance. Honest cowboys now "went on the rustle" in a quiet way, and often found the community in secret sympathy with them. There even were "rustler towns" where it was known that a man could dispose of his beef and escape conviction if accused of changing brands. It was years before rustling was generally thought of as stealing. Just as common people sometimes say: "It's no crime to cheat the railroads," so the small owners felt that cattle rustling from the corporations was no more than a just reprisal. Not until rustling was professionalized by bandits and bad men did public sentiment change and approve their extermination.

SAM STACK TREE. A saddle.

SAVVIED. This useful word, adopted into Western slang in this degenerate form, comes from the Spanish verb *saber,* to understand or know. The third person singular is *sabe.* When the word was Englished it kept the Spanish softening of *b* to *v,* but lost, and more's the pity, the round Spanish *ah.*

I have heard Chinese cooks in the West say: "Me no savvy."

SLEEPER. A calf that is earmarked but not branded is a sleeper.

SLICK EAR. A calf that has not yet been earmarked is a slick ear.

SWALLOW FORK. There were different practices on the range for marking the ears of young cattle. The outriders slashed the ears of calves that would be weaned before the round-up, so as to hold them for the owner. Or they earmarked whenever a branding iron was not handy. Calves that were following their mothers at the round-up were earmarked and branded at the same time.

The swallow fork was made by chipping a piece out of the end of the calf's ear in the shape of a swallow's tail.

TAPS. *See* Terrapin Shell.

TARP. The canvas tarpaulin has a dozen uses; it may be furled on three sticks as a tent; it enfolds the mountainous pack; it is the next best thing to a bed indoors. I was a small girl when my father taught me how to spread it over a mattress of long-needled pine and tuck it around the blankets. No eiderdown sleeping-bag was ever cosier than our well-made camp beds, with the tarps shedding every kind of weather—mountain wind and cold, summer rain, and autumn snow.

TERRAPIN SHELL. This is one of the cowboy's affectionate slang words for his saddle, his most dearly prized possession. It is his workbench, his rocking-chair, his pillow. Each man values his own saddle above any other, not only for sentiment's sake, but also because, once broken in, it actually takes on the contours of his body and becomes more comfortable for his careless, relaxed posture than another man's could be. It is the one thing which cowboys seldom gamble, hock, or sell; "He's sold his saddle" is the utmost in degradation.

Everyone knows what a Western saddle looks like, but perhaps some explanation of why it looks that way would be interesting. Its cantle must be high enough to hold the rider when the wise old cow hoss squats down on his haunches to brace against the rope. The horn must be big enough to hold the lasso when the business end is around a cow's neck and the home end is wrapped around it as around a hitching-post. The space between must be large enough for the man and his work; he must have room to "take his wraps" around the horn. The large skirt is meant to protect the pony's barrel from the lacerating cactus and chaparral. The shape of the tree varies according to locality and taste.

There usually are two cinches on a cowboy's saddle, in which case it is called a double-fire, double-rigged, or rimfire saddle. Some cowboys, however, prefer a single cinch, particularly for a breaking-saddle, when the cinch must be tightened quickly. Such a one is called a single-fire, center-fire, or California-rigged saddle. All cow hosses hate the cinch, and when they feel its merciless grip they will blow themselves full of wind. Cowboys cinch up by bracing one foot against the pony's ribs as they tighten the strap, though many riders use a loose cinch, trusting the curved saddletree and their own exquisite balance for safety.

The stirrups are made of wood or iron and attached to strong leather straps which pass over the tree just behind the horn. Usually they are adjusted by a leather thong rather than by a buckle, for the cowboy dislikes metal on his gear, except for decoration. To the scorn of Eastern riders, the stirrups are worn long, so long that the cowboy's legs are almost fully extended and he seems to stand rather than to sit in his saddle. The colloquialisms "to fork", "to hairpin" a horse, describe his posture accurately. The wooden stirrup is housed in a leather covering, the *tapadera* (Spanish), usually shortened to "tap".

The saddle is equipped with a number of convenient thongs for carrying things, usually two sets behind the cantle for the slicker, and one on either side of the pommel.

The cowboy loves decoration on his saddle, and if he cannot afford an extra forty dollars for embossed leather, or gold and "pin-wheeling"—the almost certainly fatal forward and upward plunge that lands him on his back and pins the luckless rider under the saddle horn. Most derisive of all is the term "crow hops", applied to the short, stiff-legged jumps of a horse who isn't feeling up to much bucking.

silver ornaments, he adorns it himself with brass tacks or rattlesnake skins applied with their own glue. Mexican saddles are particularly ornate.

TWINE. *See* Lasso.

WHING DING. Every maneuver of a bucking horse has been catalogued by the cowboys in slang phrases that often are brilliantly descriptive. In my part of the country a Whing Ding is a bit of playful bucking indulged in by both horse and man in a spirit of fun. Other terms are "straight bucking", when the horse pitches on one spot; "pitches a-plunging", when he runs as he bucks; "jackknifing", when he comes down with his four legs close together; "sunfishing", when he stands on his hind legs and tries to "paw the white out of the moon" while twisting his body viciously;

INDEX OF FIRST LINES